The Open University

MST125
Essential mathematics 2

# Book A

This publication forms part of an Open University module. Details of this and other Open University modules can be obtained from Student Recruitment, The Open University, PO Box 197, Milton Keynes MK7 6BJ, United Kingdom (tel. +44 (0)300 303 5303; email general-enquiries@open.ac.uk).

Alternatively, you may visit the Open University website at www.open.ac.uk where you can learn more about the wide range of modules and packs offered at all levels by The Open University.

The Open University, Walton Hall, Milton Keynes, MK7 6AA.

First published 2014. Second edition 2016.

Copyright © 2014, 2016 The Open University

All rights reserved. No part of this publication may be reproduced, stored in a retrieval system, transmitted or utilised in any form or by any means, electronic, mechanical, photocopying, recording or otherwise, without written permission from the publisher or a licence from the Copyright Licensing Agency Ltd. Details of such licences (for reprographic reproduction) may be obtained from the Copyright Licensing Agency Ltd, Saffron House, 6–10 Kirby Street, London EC1N 8TS (website www.cla.co.uk).

Open University materials may also be made available in electronic formats for use by students of the University. All rights, including copyright and related rights and database rights, in electronic materials and their contents are owned by or licensed to The Open University, or otherwise used by The Open University as permitted by applicable law.

In using electronic materials and their contents you agree that your use will be solely for the purposes of following an Open University course of study or otherwise as licensed by The Open University or its assigns.

Except as permitted above you undertake not to copy, store in any medium (including electronic storage or use in a website), distribute, transmit or retransmit, broadcast, modify or show in public such electronic materials in whole or in part without the prior written consent of The Open University or in accordance with the Copyright, Designs and Patents Act 1988.

Edited, designed and typeset by The Open University, using the Open University TeX System.

Printed in the United Kingdom by Latimer Trend and Company Ltd, Plymouth.

ISBN 978 1 4730 0345 3

2.1

# Contents

# Contents

# Welcome to MST125

In this module you'll study a wide range of topics from different areas of mathematics, and learn how many of them can be applied to practical problems. Familiarity with these topics will provide you with a firm foundation for further studies in mathematics and other mathematically rich subjects such as physics and engineering.

This module builds on the mathematical ideas developed in *Essential mathematics 1* (MST124), and is designed to be studied either after MST124 or at the same time as it. If you are studying the two modules with the same start date, or overlapping, then make sure that you read the important information in the box at the end of this Welcome section, and the further details in the appropriate section of the MST125 *Guide*.

Here are some of the topics that you'll meet in MST125.

**Number theory**, a branch of mathematics concerned with properties of the integers. You'll learn about a powerful calculating system called *modular arithmetic*, and see how this system can be used to detect errors in ISBNs (international standard book numbers) and create ciphers for disguising sensitive messages.

**Conics**, a family of curves that includes circles, ellipses, parabolas and hyperbolas. You'll see how these curves can be described geometrically and algebraically. You'll also learn how to represent conics and other curves by using *parametric equations*.

**Geometric transformations**, which include reflections, rotations and translations, and various other ways of manipulating geometric figures. You'll work with these using an algebraic approach, involving matrices and vectors.

**Proof**, where you'll look at how mathematical statements can be clearly expressed, and learn about various methods that you can use to prove that a statement is true, or show that it is false.

**Combinatorics**, where you'll meet the ideas of permutations and combinations and learn how to solve problems involving counting, such as how many different ways there are to choose a certain number of objects from a set.

**Differential equations**, which are equations that involve an unknown function and one or more of its derivatives. Such equations often arise in situations where the rate of change of a quantity depends on how much of the quantity there is, such as in radioactive decay or population modelling.

**Mechanics**, where you'll analyse the forces that act on objects, and study the motion that may be produced as a result.

You'll also have the opportunity to improve your skills in problem solving, calculus and mathematical communication, and learn how to produce properly formatted typed mathematics. You'll continue to develop your skills in using the computer algebra system introduced in MST124.

This module includes a range of topics from both pure and applied mathematics. Broadly, pure mathematics is the mathematics of abstract concepts, or mathematics that's studied for its own sake, whereas applied mathematics deals with methods and models that can be used to solve real-world problems, typically in science, engineering and economics. Number theory, for example, is normally considered to be a topic in pure mathematics, whereas mechanics is a topic in applied mathematics. However, there isn't a rigid dividing line between the two areas. Many topics, such as calculus, are relevant to both. Also, topics from pure mathematics sometimes have applications in applied mathematics, and areas of study in pure mathematics are often inspired by problems from applied mathematics. Over recent years several topics in pure mathematics, particularly in number theory and combinatorics, have been found to have important applications in areas such as computer science. This type of mathematics is different from traditional applied mathematics and is sometimes referred to as 'applicable mathematics'.

If you have finished studying MST124, or if you have never studied MST124 and are not starting it now, then you should start your study of MST125 by working through Unit 1. Otherwise, read the important information in the box below before proceeding.

### Studying MST124 and MST125 together

If you are studying MST124 and MST125 with the same start date, then you should omit Unit 1 of MST125. It provides revision of material taught in MST124, so is not suitable or necessary for you at this stage. Also, you should not study the MST124 and MST125 units on the dates shown on the main MST124 and MST125 study planners. Instead, you should follow the MST124 and MST125 joint study planner, which is available from the 'Study resources' area of the MST124 and MST125 websites. This is important because you will not be prepared to study many of the topics in MST125 if you have not already studied the related topics in MST124. The joint study planner ensures that you study the units of the two modules interleaved in the correct order. As you meet new ideas in MST124, you may find it helpful to use the activities in MST125 Unit 1 as further practice.

If you started studying MST124 a few months ago and are now starting MST125, with the two modules overlapping, then you may find it helpful to study Sections 1 to 4 of MST125 Unit 1 now, as revision, and allow some time later to study Sections 5 and 6 before you study MST125 Unit 7, *Topics in calculus*. You should study the MST124 and MST125 units at the times shown on the main, individual study planners.

Unit 1

# Key techniques

# Introduction

This unit revises the key techniques that you will need in order to study MST125 successfully. It summarises many of the important mathematical ideas and results from the underpinning module MST124 *Essential Mathematics 1*.

If you are starting MST125 at the same time as MST124 or with start dates a few months apart, then you should omit all or some of this unit at this stage. Please make sure that you have read the important information in the box in the *Welcome* section at the start of this book.

If you have completed your study of MST124 or have never studied MST124 and are not starting it now, then you are strongly advised to work through this unit as thoroughly as you can, so that you feel confident with the mathematical skills needed for MST125. As this is a revision unit, you are not expected to work through all of the material included here; instead, you should concentrate on those topics you most need to revise. The unit contains short quizzes to help you identify these topics. Sections 5 and 6 on differentiation and integration are particularly important.

For some of the activities in MST125 it is assumed that you have experience in working with the computer algebra system used in MST124. The skills that you will need are described in Section 7.

In this unit, you will review how to use some important mathematical tools.

Each of the first six sections of this unit contains:

- a short quiz to help you to identify the topics that you need to revise
- summaries of the key ideas in some topics
- several activities for you to try.

For each section, you should work through the quiz first, without referring to other materials or using the computer algebra system. If you are unable to complete a question correctly, then you will need to work through the text and activities in the corresponding subsection thoroughly. References to the relevant subsections are given in the solutions to the quiz.

You may also find it helpful to refer back to the relevant sections of the MST124 units, provided on the module website. The start of each section and subsection of this unit contain references to these.

Even if you complete the quiz questions successfully on your first attempt, you are advised to read through the section quickly as revision and then try some of the later parts of the activities in each subsection, if you have time, as a further check that you understand the material.

Some activities ask you to use standard mathematical techniques to solve problems, while others challenge your understanding by asking you to link different mathematical ideas together or to explore an idea in greater depth. Whatever the type of activity, you should write out your own solution and then compare it carefully with the solution given in this unit, paying particular attention both to the accuracy of your solution and the way it is presented. Check that your solution contains a similar level of detail to the one provided. For further practice, try the questions in the online practice quiz for this unit (on the module website).

This unit does not revise *all* the topics in MST124. You may find it helpful to have your *Handbook* available, so that you can check definitions and the mathematical summaries easily. (The *Handbook* for MST125 contains summaries of all the MST124 units as well as the MST125 units.)

If a lot of the topics in this unit are new to you or if you find them difficult, then contact either your tutor or your Student Support Team for advice as soon as possible.

# 1 Functions

This section summarises some of the key ideas about functions that are explained more fully in MST124 Unit 3. It assumes that you are familiar with the basic properties and graphs of linear, quadratic, logarithmic and exponential functions. If you are not confident with these topics, then you should work through Subsection 1.6 and Section 4 of MST124 Unit 3 before studying this section.

Now try the following quiz to determine which topics in this section you need to revise thoroughly. If you are unable to complete any part of this quiz correctly, then you should study the corresponding subsection in depth and complete the associated activities. References to the subsections are given in the solutions.

**Activity 1**   *Functions quiz*

(a)  Explain how the graph of the function
$$f(x) = -2(x+1)^2 + 8$$
can be obtained by translating and scaling the graph of $g(x) = x^2$.

Sketch the graph of $f$.

Label the vertex and the coordinates of the points where the graph crosses the axes.

(b)  Hence find the image set of the function
$$h(x) = -2(x+1)^2 + 8 \quad (-2 < x \le 1).$$

(c)  Does the function $h$ have an inverse function? Justify your answer.

(d)  Find the rule of the inverse function of the function
$$k(x) = 3x - 2.$$

Sketch the graphs of the functions $k$ and $k^{-1}$ together, using the same scale on both axes.

(e) Find the rules of the following composite functions, where $f$ and $k$ are the functions defined in parts (a) and (d).

    (i) $k \circ k$    (ii) $f \circ k$    (iii) $k \circ f$

## 1.1 Functions and their graphs

> For more detail on the topics covered in this subsection, refer to Section 1 of MST124 Unit 3.

Informally, you can think of a function as a process that converts each input value in a given set of values into an output value. For example, suppose the process 'square the number' is applied to all the real numbers between (and including) 0 and 2. Consider the input value 0.5. Its output value is $(0.5)^2 = 0.25$. If the process is applied to all the input values, then the output values are the real numbers that lie between (and including) 0 and 4.

If you use the right ingredients and follow the recipe, you'll get the right result – just like with a function!

More formally, a **function** consists of:

- a set of allowed input values, called the **domain** of the function
- a set of values in which every output value lies, called the **codomain** of the function
- a process, called the **rule** of the function, for converting each input value into *exactly one* output value.

Suppose the squaring function described above is denoted by $f$. Then its rule and domain can be written as

$$f(x) = x^2 \quad (0 \le x \le 2).$$

For each input value, there is exactly one output value, which is called the **image** of the input value. The set of output values of a function is called the **image set** of the function. For example, the image set of $f$ is the set of all real numbers that lie between (and including) 0 and 4.

Figure 1 illustrates the domain, codomain and rule of a function, a typical input value $x$, its image $f(x)$, and the image set.

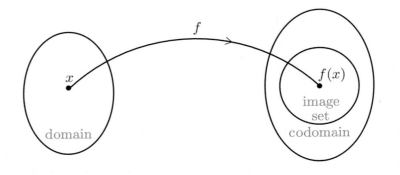

**Figure 1**   A function and its image set

In this unit, you will be working only with functions whose domains and codomains are sets of real numbers. However, there are other types of functions, such as functions for which the domain and/or the codomain is a set of another type of numbers (for example, complex numbers), or a set of points in the plane. You will meet some other types of functions later in your study of MST125.

For some functions, the codomain and image set are identical. However, working out the image set of a function can sometimes be difficult and time-consuming. So when a function is specified, often the codomain is chosen to be a set that contains the image set and may contain other values as well. For example, in this module, for a function that has a domain consisting of real numbers, the codomain is assumed to be the set of all real numbers, $\mathbb{R}$, unless specified otherwise.

When you specify a function, it is important to consider the domain carefully and check that the rule can be applied to each input value. For example, consider the rule

$$h(x) = \frac{1}{x}.$$

In this case, $x = 0$ should be excluded from the domain, as it is not possible to work out $1/x$ when $x = 0$. The function with this rule and the largest possible domain of real numbers is

$$h(x) = \frac{1}{x} \quad (x \neq 0).$$

Sometimes a function is specified by *just a rule*. In this case, it is understood that the domain of the function is the largest possible set of values for which the rule is applicable.

Note that the rule must define *exactly one* output value for each allowed input value. So, for example,

$$g(x) = \pm\sqrt{x} \quad (x > 0)$$

does *not* define a function, since $\pm\sqrt{x}$ specifies two output values, $\sqrt{x}$ and $-\sqrt{x}$, for each allowed input value $x$. (Remember that the symbol $\sqrt{x}$ always means the *non-negative* square root of $x$.)

**Activity 2**  *Rules that do not specify functions*

Explain why each of the following rules cannot be used to specify a function with domain and codomain $\mathbb{R}$.

(a)  $f(x) = \dfrac{4}{2x - 3}$      (b)  $m(t) = t \pm 3$      (c)  $s(p) = \sqrt{p^2 - 4p - 12}$

An **interval** is a set of real numbers that corresponds to a part of the number line that you can draw 'without lifting your pen from the paper'. A number that lies at the end of an interval is called an **endpoint**.

Often the domain of a function is the set of real numbers, $\mathbb{R}$, or part of this set, such as an interval. If the interval includes all of its endpoints, then the interval is said to be **closed**; if none of its endpoints are included, then the interval is said to be **open**. If one endpoint is included and the other is not, the interval is said to be **half-open** or **half-closed**. Intervals can be specified by using inequality signs, such as $-8 \le x < 2$, or by using interval notation such as $[-8, 2)$. A square bracket indicates that an endpoint is included in the interval and a round bracket indicates that it is not.

An interval that extends indefinitely is denoted by using the symbol $\infty$ (which is read as 'infinity'), or its 'negative', $-\infty$ (which is read as 'minus infinity'), in place of an endpoint. The set of real numbers $\mathbb{R}$ is an interval with no endpoints, so it is said to be both open and closed!

Intervals can be illustrated on the number line as shown in the box below. A solid dot indicates that the value is included in the interval and a hollow dot indicates that it is not.

---

**Interval notation**

**Open intervals**

| $(a, b)$ | $(a, \infty)$ | $(-\infty, b)$ | $(-\infty, \infty)$ |
|---|---|---|---|
| $a < x < b$ | $x > a$ | $x < b$ | $\mathbb{R}$ |

**Closed intervals**

| $[a, b]$ | $[a, \infty)$ | $(-\infty, b]$ | $(-\infty, \infty)$ | $\{a\}$ |
|---|---|---|---|---|
| $a \le x \le b$ | $x \ge a$ | $x \le b$ | $\mathbb{R}$ | $x = a$ |

**Half-open (or half-closed) intervals**

| $[a, b)$ | $(a, b]$ |
|---|---|
| $a \le x < b$ | $a < x \le b$ |

---

A set may consist of two or more intervals. In such cases, the set notation for the **union** of two sets (namely $\cup$) can be used. For example, the largest possible domain of real numbers of the function with rule

$$h(x) = \frac{1}{x}$$

consists of the two intervals $(-\infty, 0)$ and $(0, \infty)$, so this domain can be written as

$$(-\infty, 0) \cup (0, \infty).$$

You may also see domains and codomains specified using the 'is in' symbol, $\in$. For example,

$$x \in [2, 3] \quad \text{means} \quad 2 \le x \le 3.$$

A function $f$ with rule $f(x) = x^2$ and domain $[0, 2]$ can be written as

$$f(x) = x^2 \quad (x \in [0, 2]).$$

### Activity 3   Identifying domains of functions

Describe the largest possible domain of real numbers for each of the following rules, and specify the domain using set notation.

(a)  $g(t) = \sqrt{t - 4}$     (b)  $h(u) = \dfrac{u + 1}{u^2 - 4}$

One way of visualising a function is to sketch its **graph**. The graph of a function $f$ is the set of points $(x, y)$, where $x$ is a value in the domain and $y$ is the corresponding image, $f(x)$.

To sketch the graph of a function whose domain is not the largest set of numbers for which the function's rule is applicable, first sketch the graph on the largest possible set and then erase the parts of the graph for values of $x$ outside the domain. With practice, you should be able to sketch the graph of the function directly, without having to sketch a larger graph first.

For example, if the function is

$$f(x) = x + 2 \quad (1 \le x < 3),$$

then the rule is applicable for all real numbers, but the domain of $f$ is the interval $[1, 3)$. So the graph of $f$ is the portion of the line $y = x + 2$ for values of $x$ from 1, up to but not including 3, as shown in Figure 2.

Note that the point $(1, 3)$ is included in the graph, so it is marked with a solid dot, whereas the point $(3, 5)$ is excluded from the graph, so it is marked with a hollow dot.

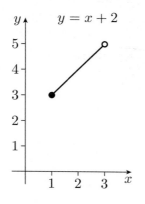

**Figure 2** The graph of $f(x) = x + 2$ $(1 \leq x < 3)$

Drawing the graph of a function can often help you determine the image set of that function. To find the image set of a function using its graph, you can follow these steps:

1. Mark the domain on the $x$-axis.

2. Draw the graph for the values of $x$ in the domain.

3. Mark the set of $y$-coordinates of the graph on the $y$-axis. This is the image set.

This process is illustrated in Figure 3. Note that the images of the endpoints of the domain are not necessarily the endpoints of the image set.

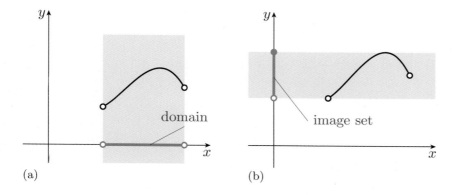

(a)　　　　　　　　　　(b)

**Figure 3** (a) The domain of a function marked on the horizontal axis (b) the image set marked on the vertical axis

Figure 4 shows the graph of the function

$$f(x) = 2x^2 - 4x + 5 \quad (0 < x \leq 3),$$

with its image set marked on the $y$-axis.

The smallest value in the image set is the $y$-coordinate of the vertex, and the largest value in the image set is $f(3)$. Hence the image set of $f$ is the interval $[3, 11]$. This is not the same as the interval between the images of the endpoints of the domain, which is $(5, 11]$.

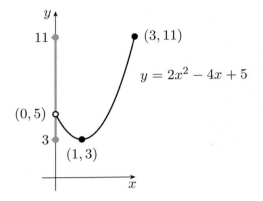

**Figure 4** The graph of $f(x) = 2x^2 - 4x + 5 \quad (0 < x \le 3)$

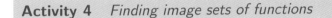

**Activity 4** *Finding image sets of functions*

(a) Sketch the graph of the function
$$f(x) = 3x - 4 \quad (-0.5 < x \le 2)$$
and hence find its image set.

(b) The graphs of two functions are shown below. In each case, use the graph to find the image set of the function.

(i) $f(x) = -x^2 - 2x + 3 \quad (-2 \le x < 1)$

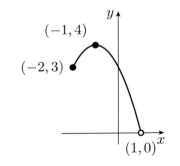

(ii) $f(x) = 2x^3 - 3x^2 - 12x + 4 \quad (-2 \le x \le 3)$

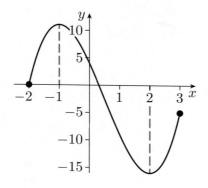

## 1.2 Translating and scaling graphs of functions

For more detail on the topics covered in this subsection, refer to Section 2 of MST124 Unit 3.

By translating and scaling the graphs of some standard functions (such as $y = mx + c$, $y = x^2$, $y = |x|$, $y = \ln x$ and $y = a^x$), you can sketch the graphs of many more functions.

Informally, if a graph is translated, it is shifted to a new position without rotating, reflecting or distorting it in any way. The box below explains how to obtain the graphs of new functions by translating the graphs of standard functions.

### Translations of graphs

Suppose that $f$ is a function and $c$ is a constant. To obtain the graph of:

- $y = f(x) + c$, translate the graph of $y = f(x)$ up by $c$ units (the translation is down if $c$ is negative)

- $y = f(x - c)$, translate the graph of $y = f(x)$ to the right by $c$ units (the translation is to the left if $c$ is negative).

These effects are illustrated in Figure 5.

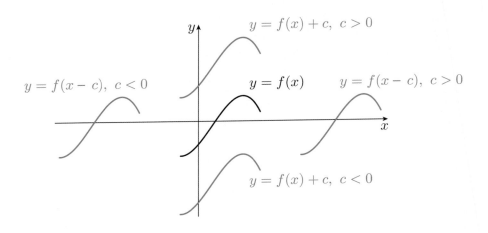

**Figure 5**   Pieces of graphs of equations of the form $y = f(x) + c$ and $y = f(x - c)$

For example, to obtain the graph of:

- $y = x^2 + 3$, translate the graph of $y = x^2$ by 3 units upwards
- $y = |x| - 4$, translate the graph of $y = |x|$ by 4 units downwards
- $y = (x - 2)^3$, translate the graph of $y = x^3$ by 2 units to the right
- $y = (x + 4)^3$, translate the graph of $y = x^3$ by 4 units to the left. (The equation can be written as $y = (x - (-4))^3$.)

**Activity 5**   *Translating graphs*

In this activity you will apply translations to the graph of $f(x) = 1/x$, shown below.

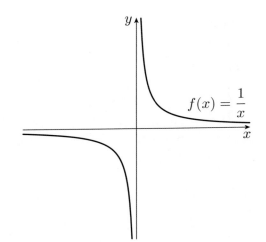

(a) For each of the following functions, describe how you could obtain its graph by applying translations to the graph of $f(x) = 1/x$, and then sketch the graph. Your sketch should show the axes, and the shape and position of the graph, but you need not work out the $x$- or $y$-intercepts.

    (i)  $g(x) = \dfrac{1}{x} + 2$      (ii)  $h(x) = \dfrac{1}{x + 2}$

(b) Show that

$$\frac{3x - 5}{x - 2} = \frac{1}{x - 2} + 3.$$

    Hence sketch the graph of the function $q(x) = \dfrac{3x - 5}{x - 2}$.

Another way to obtain the graphs of new functions is by scaling the graphs of standard functions.

Consider the graph of the equation $y = cf(x)$, where $f$ is a function of $x$ and $c$ is a constant. In this case, the $y$-coordinate of each point on the graph of $y = f(x)$ is multiplied by the factor $c$. For example, if $c = 2$, then each $y$-coordinate is doubled. This has the effect of scaling the graph by the factor 2 in the $y$-direction.

In general, the graph of $y = cf(x)$ can be obtained by scaling the graph of $y = f(x)$ by the factor $c$ in the $y$-direction. Note that if $c$ is negative, then the new graph is obtained by first scaling by the factor $|c|$ and then reflecting the scaled graph in the $x$-axis.

**Vertical scalings of graphs**

Suppose that $c$ is a constant. To obtain the graph of $y = cf(x)$, scale the graph of $y = f(x)$ vertically by a factor of $c$.

These effects are illustrated in Figure 6.

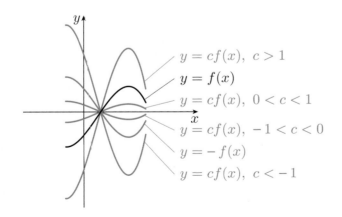

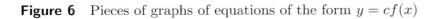

**Figure 6**   Pieces of graphs of equations of the form $y = cf(x)$

Graphs can also be scaled horizontally.

> **Horizontal scalings of graphs**
>
> Suppose that $c$ is a *non-zero* constant. To obtain the graph of $y = f\left(\dfrac{x}{c}\right)$, scale the graph of $y = f(x)$ horizontally by a factor of $c$.

These effects are illustrated in Figure 7.

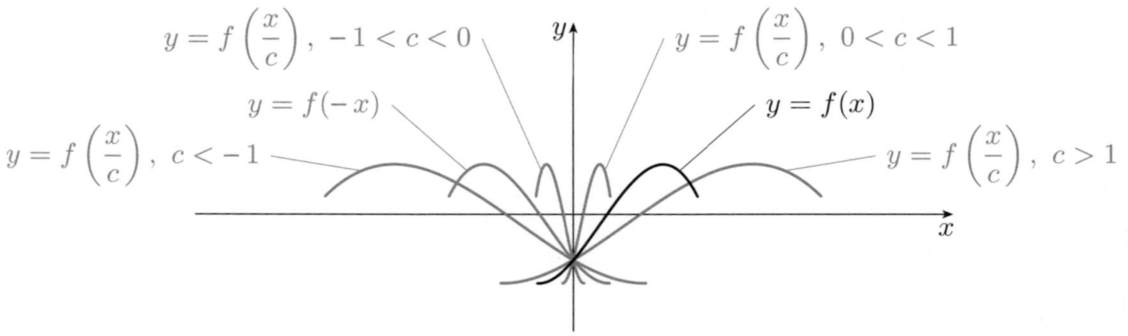

$$y = f\left(\frac{x}{c}\right),\ -1 < c < 0 \qquad y = f\left(\frac{x}{c}\right),\ 0 < c < 1$$

$$y = f(-x) \qquad\qquad y = f(x)$$

$$y = f\left(\frac{x}{c}\right),\ c < -1 \qquad\qquad y = f\left(\frac{x}{c}\right),\ c > 1$$

**Figure 7**   Pieces of graphs of equations of the form $y = f\left(\dfrac{x}{c}\right)$

Note in particular the effect on the graph if the scaling factor $c$ is $-1$. In this case, the graph of the new equation, $y = f(-x)$, is obtained by reflecting the graph of $y = f(x)$ in the $y$-axis.

In general, if the scaling factor $c$ is negative, then you can obtain the graph of the new equation, $y = f(x/c)$, by first scaling the original graph by the factor $|c|$ in the $x$-direction and then reflecting the graph in the $y$-axis. For example, if the graph of $y = \sin x$ is scaled by a factor of $-0.5$ in the $x$-direction, then the graph will be scaled by a factor of $0.5$ in the $x$-direction and then reflected in the $y$-axis, as shown in Figure 8. The equation of the scaled graph is

$$y = \sin(-x/0.5) = \sin(-2x),\ \text{or}\ y = -\sin(2x),$$

since for any $\theta$, $\sin(-\theta) = -\sin\theta$.

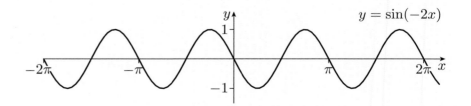

**Figure 8**   The graph of $y = \sin x$ after it has been scaled by a factor of $0.5$ in the $x$-direction and then reflected in the $y$-axis

## Activity 6   Scaling graphs horizontally and vertically

(a) Explain how to obtain the graph of each of the following functions by scaling the graph of $f(x) = e^x$.

   (i) $g(x) = -3e^x$      (ii) $h(x) = e^{2x}$      (iii) $k(x) = e^{x-1}$

(b) For each of the following functions, write down the equation of the graph obtained by applying the given scaling factor to the graph of the function.

   (i)   $f(x) = x^2$, scaling factor $\frac{1}{3}$ vertically.

   (ii)  $g(x) = \ln x$, scaling factor $2$ horizontally.

   (iii) $h(x) = \cos x$, scaling factor $-\frac{1}{2}$ in the $x$-direction.

   (iv)  $k(x) = e^x$, scaling factor $\frac{2}{3}$ in the $y$-direction, followed by a reflection in the $x$-axis.

Sometimes you can obtain the graph of a function by applying more than one translation or scaling to the graph of a standard function.

For example:

- The graph of $y = 5x^2 - 3$ can be obtained by first scaling the graph of $y = x^2$ by the factor $5$ in the $y$-direction to get the graph of $y = 5x^2$, then translating this graph by 3 units downwards.

- The graph of $y = 5(x - 3)^2$ can be obtained by first translating the graph of $y = x^2$ by 3 units to the right to get the graph of $y = (x - 3)^2$, then scaling this graph by the factor $5$ in the $y$-direction.

- The graph of $y = 5(x^2 - 3)$ can be obtained by first translating the graph of $y = x^2$ by 3 units downwards to get the graph of $y = x^2 - 3$, then scaling this graph by the factor $5$ in the $y$-direction.

These three graphs are shown in Figure 9.

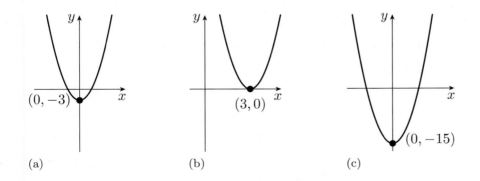

(a)                 (b)                 (c)

**Figure 9**   The graphs of (a) $y = 5x^2 - 3$ (b) $y = 5(x - 3)^2$ and (c) $y = 5(x^2 - 3)$

Note that graph (a), in which the scaling was applied first, followed by the translation, is different from graph (c), in which the translation was applied first, followed by the scaling.

**Activity 7**  *Translating and scaling graphs*

For each of the following equations, describe how you could obtain its graph by applying scalings and translations to the graph of $y = x^3$, which is shown below. Then sketch the graph, showing the $y$-intercept and the coordinates of the new position of the point $P$. (For this activity, you need not show the $x$-intercept.)

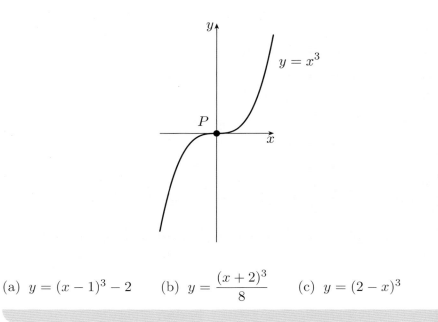

(a)  $y = (x - 1)^3 - 2$     (b)  $y = \dfrac{(x + 2)^3}{8}$     (c)  $y = (2 - x)^3$

## 1.3  Composite functions

> For more detail on the topics covered in this subsection, refer to Subsection 3.2 of MST124 Unit 3.

Suppose that $f$ and $g$ are functions. The **composite function** $g \circ f$ is the function whose rule is

$$(g \circ f)(x) = g(f(x)),$$

and whose domain consists of all the values $x$ in the domain of $f$ such that $f(x)$ is in the domain of $g$. The symbol $\circ$ is read as 'circle' or 'composed with'.

For example, suppose that

$$f(x) = 5x^2 \quad \text{and} \quad g(x) = x - 3.$$

The function $f$ squares the input value and then multiplies the square by 5, and the function $g$ takes the input value $5x^2$ and subtracts 3, as illustrated in Figure 10.

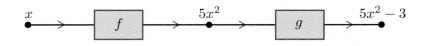

**Figure 10**   The composite function $(g \circ f)(x) = 5x^2 - 3$

That is, the rule of the composite function $g \circ f$ is

$$(g \circ f)(x) = g(f(x)) = g(5x^2) = 5x^2 - 3.$$

Note that the domain of each of the functions $f$ and $g$ is $\mathbb{R}$, and the image set of $f$ is the interval $[0, \infty)$, which is a subset of the domain of $g$. Hence the domain of the composite function $g \circ f$ is $\mathbb{R}$.

The composite function $f \circ g$ can also be formed. The rule of this composite function is

$$(f \circ g)(x) = f(g(x)) = f(x - 3) = 5(x - 3)^2.$$

The image set of $g$ is $\mathbb{R}$, which is the same as the domain of $f$, so the domain of $f \circ g$ is also $\mathbb{R}$.

Note that the rules for the two composite functions $g \circ f$ and $f \circ g$ are different. This is expressed by saying that composition of functions is not commutative.

So the order in which a composite function is written down is important. Two or more functions making up a composite function are applied in order, from the function written on the right to the function written on the left. For example, for the functions $f$, $g$ and $h$, the composite of $f$ followed by $g$ followed by $h$ is written

$$h \circ g \circ f.$$

## Activity 8   *Composing functions*

Suppose that

$$f(x) = 2x - 1 \quad \text{and} \quad g(x) = 4 - x^2.$$

Find the rule of each of the following composite functions.

(a) $f \circ g$      (b) $g \circ f$      (c) $g \circ f \circ f$

## 1.4  Inverse functions

For more detail on the topics covered in this subsection, refer to Subsection 3.3 of MST124 Unit 3.

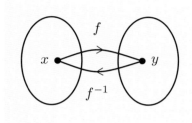

**Figure 11**  A mapping diagram illustrating a function $f$ and its inverse function $f^{-1}$

Essentially, the **inverse function** of a function $f$ is the function that 'undoes' the effect of $f$. It is denoted by $f^{-1}$. If inputting a number $x$ to $f$ gives the number $y$, then inputting the number $y$ to $f^{-1}$ gives the original number $x$, as illustrated in Figure 11. For example, if $f$ is the function $f(x) = x + 4$, then inputting 3 to $f$ gives 7, and inputting 7 to $f^{-1}$ gives 3. Since the function $f$ adds 4 to each value, the inverse function, $f^{-1}$, which undoes this action, subtracts 4 from each value, that is $f^{-1}(x) = x - 4$.

Some functions do not have inverses. For example, the squaring function $f(x) = x^2$ gives $f(2) = 4$ and $f(-2) = 4$, so both 2 and $-2$ have the same output 4. If you try to undo $f$, then for the input value, 4, there are two possible output values, 2 and $-2$, not one value, as is required for a function. So, in this case the inverse function of $f$ does not exist. If you can find two or more input numbers that give the same output value, then the function does not have an inverse.

This is expressed by saying that only functions that are *one-to-one* have inverse functions. Informally, a function is one-to-one if it sends different input values to different output values.

Formally, a function $f$ is said to be **one-to-one** if, for all numbers $x_1$ and $x_2$ in its domain such that $x_1 \neq x_2$, then

$$f(x_1) \neq f(x_2).$$

A useful way to recognise whether a function is one-to-one (and hence has an inverse) is to look at its graph. If you can draw a horizontal line that crosses the graph more than once, then the function is not one-to-one.

Figure 12(a) shows the graph of a function where any horizontal line you draw crosses the graph at most once. The function is therefore one-to-one and has an inverse. On the other hand, Figure 12(b) shows that the two input values marked as $x_1$ and $x_2$ have the same output value, indicated by the value at which the dashed horizontal line intersects the $y$-axis. So this function is not one-to-one and hence does not have an inverse.

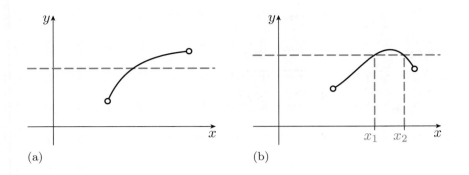

(a)                              (b)

**Figure 12**   The graphs of (a) a one-to-one function, and (b) a function that is not one-to-one

Here is another useful way to recognise a one-to-one function. If a function is either increasing on its whole domain or decreasing on its whole domain, then it is one-to-one and therefore has an inverse function. The box below reminds you what it means to say that a function is increasing or decreasing.

**Functions increasing or decreasing on an interval**

A function $f$ is **increasing on the interval** $I$ if for all values $x_1$ and $x_2$ in $I$ such that $x_1 < x_2$,

$$f(x_1) < f(x_2).$$

A function $f$ is **decreasing on the interval** $I$ if for all values $x_1$ and $x_2$ in $I$ such that $x_1 < x_2$,

$$f(x_1) > f(x_2).$$

(The interval $I$ must be part of the domain of $f$.)

Since an inverse function undoes the original function:

- The domain of an inverse function is the image set of the original function.

- The image set of an inverse function is the domain of the original function.

- The rule for an inverse function can be found by rearranging the rule for the original function.

Suppose $(a, b)$ is a point on the graph of the original function $f$; that is, $b$ is the output value that $f$ gives for the input value $a$. Since the inverse function takes $b$ as the input value and gives the output value $a$, the point $(b, a)$ is a point on the graph of the inverse function. If the scales on the axes are equal, then the point $(b, a)$ is the reflection of the point $(a, b)$ in the line $y = x$, as illustrated in Figure 13.

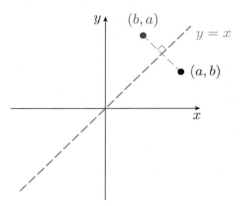

**Figure 13**   Reflection of $(a, b)$ in the line $y = x$, on a graph with equal scales on the axes

So, to obtain the graph of the inverse function, draw the graph of the original function on axes with equal scales, then reflect this graph in the line $y = x$. The reflected graph is the graph of the inverse function, as illustrated in Figure 14.

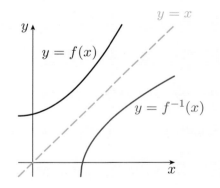

**Figure 14**   The graph of a function $f(x)$ and its inverse $f^{-1}(x)$, with equal scales on the axes

The next example illustrates how to find an inverse function and sketch its graph.

**Example 1**   *Finding an inverse function*

Does the function
$$f(x) = \frac{x}{2} + 1 \quad (x \in [-1, 4])$$

have an inverse function? If so, find it and sketch the graphs of $f$ and its inverse using axes with equal scales.

**Solution**

🔍 Sketch the graph of $f$. (For a more complicated function, it might be easier to obtain a computer plot.) 💬

The graph of $f$ is shown below.

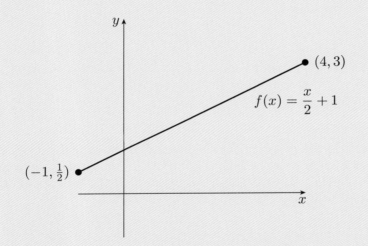

🔍 Think about whether every horizontal line that crosses the graph of $f$ does so exactly once. 💬

The graph shows that $f$ is one-to-one and therefore has an inverse function.

🔍 Rearrange the equation $f(x) = y$ to get $x$ in terms of $y$, and hence write down $f^{-1}(y) = x$. 💬

The equation $f(x) = y$ can be rearranged as follows.
$$\frac{x}{2} + 1 = y$$
$$x + 2 = 2y$$
$$x = 2y - 2.$$

So $f^{-1}(y) = 2y - 2$.

🔍 Any variable can be used in the rule, but usually the variable chosen is $x$. 💬

Changing the variable to $x$, we can rewrite the rule for the inverse function as

$$f^{-1}(x) = 2x - 2.$$

🔍 To find the domain of $f^{-1}$, find the image set of $f$, using the graph to help you. 💬

The graph shows that the image set of $f$ is $[\frac{1}{2}, 3]$.

Hence the domain of $f^{-1}$ is also $[\frac{1}{2}, 3]$.

🔍 Specify $f^{-1}$ by stating its domain and rule. 💬

So the inverse function of $f$ is the function

$$f^{-1}(x) = 2x - 2 \quad (x \in [\tfrac{1}{2}, 3]).$$

🔍 The graph of the inverse function is obtained by drawing the graph of the original function on axes with equal scales, and then reflecting it in the line $y = x$. 💬

The graphs of $f$ and $f^{-1}$ are shown below.

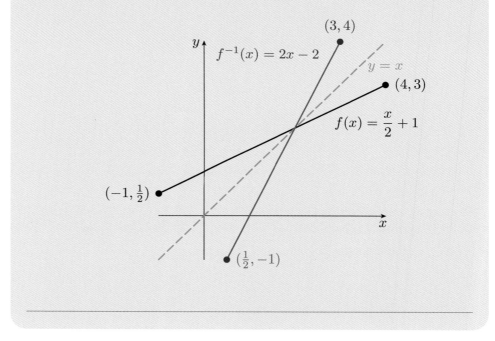

When you are working with the notation $f^{-1}$, where $f$ is a function, it is important to appreciate that it does *not* mean the function $g$ with rule

$$g(x) = (f(x))^{-1}, \quad \text{that is,} \quad g(x) = \frac{1}{f(x)}.$$

This function $g$ is called the **reciprocal** of the function $f$, and it is never denoted by $f^{-1}$.

---

**Activity 9**  *Finding inverse functions*

Determine whether each of the functions represented by the following graphs has an inverse function. If it does, then find the inverse function and sketch its graph and the graph of the original function using axes with equal scales.

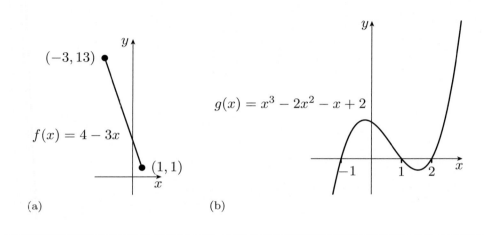

(a)   (b)

---

# 2 Trigonometry

This section summarises some of the key ideas about trigonometric functions and identities that are explained more fully in Sections 2 and 4 of MST124 Unit 4.

This section, and other sections in this unit, assume that you are familiar with the following topics from Sections 1 and 3 of MST124 Unit 4:

- using radians to specify the sizes of angles
- using Pythagoras' theorem and the trigonometric ratios for sine, cosine and tangent to find unknown side lengths and angles in right-angled triangles
- using the sine and cosine rules to find unknown side lengths and angles in triangles that do not have a right angle.

If you are not confident with these topics, then you should work through Sections 1 and 3 of MST124 Unit 4 before studying this section.

Try the following quiz to determine which topics in this section you need to revise thoroughly.

**Activity 10    *Trigonometry quiz***

(a) Find $\sin\left(\dfrac{7\pi}{4}\right)$, $\cos\left(\dfrac{7\pi}{4}\right)$ and $\tan\left(\dfrac{7\pi}{4}\right)$ without using a calculator.

(b) Use the ASTC diagram to find all solutions between $0°$ and $360°$ of the equation $\sin\theta = -\dfrac{1}{\sqrt{2}}$. Give exact answers.

(c) Use the symmetry of the graph of the cosine function to find all solutions between $-\pi$ and $\pi$ of the equation $\cos\theta = 0.3$. Give your answers to three significant figures.

(d) Suppose that $\theta$ is the acute angle with $\cos(2\theta) = \frac{3}{5}$. Use a trigonometric identity to find the exact value of $\sin\theta$. You can refer to the *Handbook* to help you choose a suitable trigonometric identity.

## 2.1  Trigonometric functions

> For more detail on the topics covered in this subsection, refer to Section 2 of MST124 Unit 4.

In this subsection you'll revise how the sine, cosine and tangent of any angle are defined and then solve some trigonometric equations.

First, consider any *acute* angle $\theta$ and its associated point $P$ on the unit circle, as illustrated in Figure 15(a). A line has been drawn from $P$ to the $x$-axis, to complete a right-angled triangle. A close-up of this triangle is shown in Figure 15(b).

Angles can be seen everywhere in an urban environment

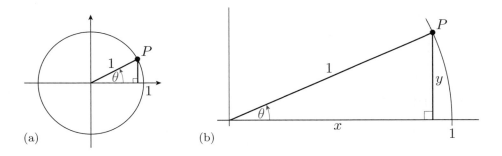

(a)          (b)

**Figure 15**    (a) The point $P$ on the unit circle associated with an acute angle $\theta$    (b) a close-up of the right-angled triangle

Suppose that the coordinates of the point $P$ are $(x, y)$. Then you can see from Figure 15 that

$$\sin \theta = \frac{\text{opp}}{\text{hyp}} = \frac{y}{1} = y$$

$$\cos \theta = \frac{\text{adj}}{\text{hyp}} = \frac{x}{1} = x$$

$$\tan \theta = \frac{\text{opp}}{\text{adj}} = \frac{y}{x}.$$

These equations are used to define the sine, cosine and tangent of *any* angle $\theta$, as follows.

> **Sine, cosine and tangent**
>
> Suppose that $\theta$ is any angle and $(x, y)$ are the coordinates of its associated point $P$ on the unit circle. Then
>
> $$\sin \theta = y, \quad \cos \theta = x,$$
>
> and, provided that $x \neq 0$,
>
> $$\tan \theta = \frac{y}{x}.$$
>
> (If $x = 0$, then $\tan \theta$ is undefined.)

Using these facts, it is straightforward to write down the sine, cosine and tangent of any angle $\theta$ whose associated point $P$ lies on one of the coordinate axes; that is, any angle that is an integer multiple of $\pi/2$. (Note that if $P$ lies on the $y$-axis, then $\tan \theta$ is not defined.)

A convenient method of working out the sine, cosine or tangent of any other angle is the following useful fact, combined with the ASTC diagram.

> Suppose that $\theta$ is an angle whose associated point $P$ does not lie on either the $x$-axis or the $y$-axis, and $\phi$ is the acute angle between $OP$ and the $x$-axis. Then
>
> $$\sin \theta = \pm \sin \phi$$
> $$\cos \theta = \pm \cos \phi$$
> $$\tan \theta = \pm \tan \phi.$$
>
> The ASTC diagram tells you which sign to apply in each case.
>
> (The values of $\sin \phi$, $\cos \phi$ and $\tan \phi$ are all positive, because $\phi$ is acute.)

The ASTC diagram is shown in Figure 16.

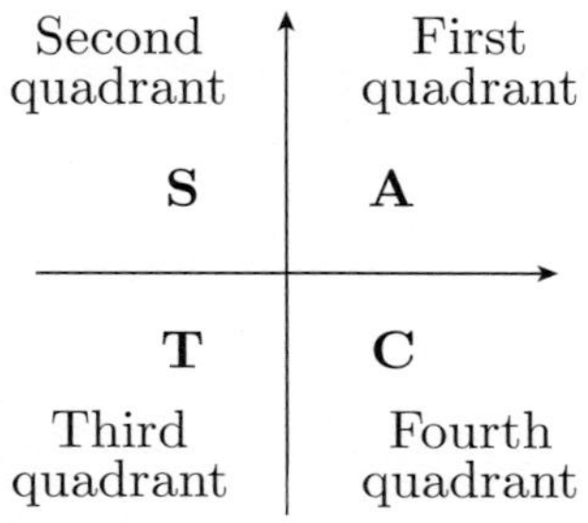

|  | | |
|:---:|:---:|:---:|
| Second quadrant | First quadrant | |
| **S** | **A** | |
| **T** | **C** | |
| Third quadrant | Fourth quadrant | |

**Figure 16** The ASTC diagram

The letter in each quadrant of the ASTC diagram indicates which of $\sin\theta$, $\cos\theta$ and $\tan\theta$ are positive when the point $P$ associated with the angle $\theta$ lies in that quadrant:

- A stands for all
- S stands for sin
- T stands for tan
- C stands for cos.

You will see later in this section that the ASTC diagram can also be useful in solving trigonometric equations.

Although you can use your calculator to work out a trigonometric value, the angles in Table 1 are used so frequently that it is worth memorising their values, or learning how to work them out quickly by sketching the relevant right-angled triangles.

**Table 1** Sine, cosine and tangent of special angles

| $\theta$ in radians | $\theta$ in degrees | $\sin\theta$ | $\cos\theta$ | $\tan\theta$ |
|:---:|:---:|:---:|:---:|:---:|
| $0$ | $0°$ | $0$ | $1$ | $0$ |
| $\dfrac{\pi}{6}$ | $30°$ | $\dfrac{1}{2}$ | $\dfrac{\sqrt{3}}{2}$ | $\dfrac{1}{\sqrt{3}}$ |
| $\dfrac{\pi}{4}$ | $45°$ | $\dfrac{1}{\sqrt{2}}$ | $\dfrac{1}{\sqrt{2}}$ | $1$ |
| $\dfrac{\pi}{3}$ | $60°$ | $\dfrac{\sqrt{3}}{2}$ | $\dfrac{1}{2}$ | $\sqrt{3}$ |
| $\dfrac{\pi}{2}$ | $90°$ | $1$ | $0$ | undefined |

The next example illustrates how to calculate the trigonometric values for an angle in the third quadrant that is related to one of the acute angles in Table 1, which will be referred to as the *special angles table*.

**Example 2** *Finding trigonometric values without using a calculator*

Use the ASTC diagram and the special angles table to find $\sin\left(\dfrac{4\pi}{3}\right)$, $\cos\left(\dfrac{4\pi}{3}\right)$ and $\tan\left(\dfrac{4\pi}{3}\right)$ without using your calculator.

**Solution**

🔍 Draw a sketch showing the required angle, marking the origin $O$ and the approximate position of the point $P$ on the unit circle corresponding to the angle. Work out the acute angle between $OP$ and the $x$-axis. 💬

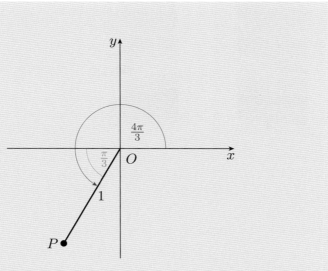

From the diagram, the acute angle that $OP$ makes with the $x$-axis is $\pi/3$.

💬 Work out the signs of the trigonometric values of the angle from the ASTC diagram. 💬

The angle $4\pi/3$ lies in the third quadrant, so the sine and cosine of this angle are negative and the tangent is positive.

Using the special angles table then gives

$$\sin\left(\frac{4\pi}{3}\right) = -\sin\left(\frac{\pi}{3}\right) = -\frac{\sqrt{3}}{2},$$

$$\cos\left(\frac{4\pi}{3}\right) = -\cos\left(\frac{\pi}{3}\right) = -\frac{1}{2}$$

and

$$\tan\left(\frac{4\pi}{3}\right) = +\tan\left(\frac{\pi}{3}\right) = \sqrt{3}.$$

**Activity 11**  *Finding trigonometric values without using a calculator*

Find the following trigonometric values without using your calculator. Give exact answers.

(a) $\cos(-3\pi)$     (b) $\tan\left(\frac{2\pi}{3}\right)$     (c) $\sin\left(-\frac{3\pi}{4}\right)$

The graphs of the sine, cosine and tangent functions can be generated by considering the coordinates of the point $P$ as it moves around the unit circle. The graph of the sine function is shown in Figure 17.

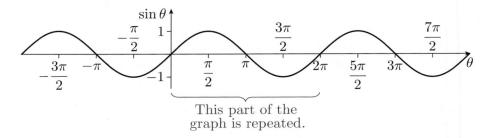

**Figure 17**    The graph of the sine function

The part of the graph between $\theta = 0$ and $\theta = 2\pi$ is repeated after every interval of $2\pi$ radians, and we say that the **period** of the graph is $2\pi$ radians.

From the symmetry of the graph, the following hold for any value of $\theta$.

$$\sin(\theta + 2n\pi) = \sin\theta, \quad \text{where } n \text{ is an integer}$$
$$\sin(-\theta) = -\sin\theta$$

The graph of the cosine function is shown in Figure 18.

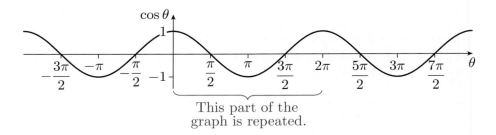

**Figure 18**    The graph of the cosine function

The period of the graph of the cosine function is $2\pi$ radians and, from the symmetry of the graph, the following hold for any value of $\theta$.

$$\cos(\theta + 2n\pi) = \cos\theta, \quad \text{where } n \text{ is an integer}$$
$$\cos(-\theta) = \cos\theta$$

The cosine graph can be obtained by translating the sine graph to the left by $\pi/2$. Hence the following also holds for any value of $\theta$.

$$\cos \theta = \sin \left( \theta + \frac{\pi}{2} \right)$$

The graph of the tangent function is shown in Figure 19.

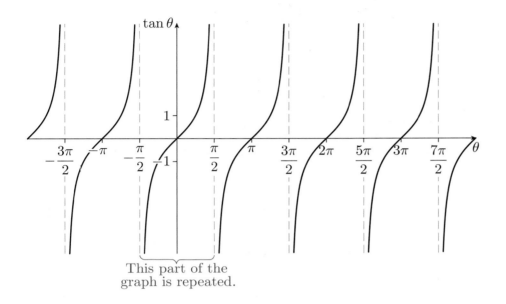

This part of the
graph is repeated.

**Figure 19** The graph of the tangent function

The vertical dashed lines drawn on the graph are asymptotes. (An **asymptote** is a straight line that a curve approaches arbitrarily closely as you trace your pen tip further and further along it away from the origin.) The asymptotes occur when $\cos \theta = 0$, that is, when $\theta = \frac{\pi}{2} + n\pi$, for some integer $n$. The tangent function is not defined for these values of $\theta$.

The graph repeats after an interval of $\pi$ radians. In other words, it is periodic with a period of $\pi$ radians.

From the symmetry of the graph, the following hold for all values of $\theta$ where $\tan \theta$ is defined.

$$\tan(\theta + n\pi) = \tan \theta, \quad \text{where } n \text{ is an integer}$$
$$\tan(-\theta) = -\tan \theta$$

The above graphs show that the sine, cosine and tangent functions are not one-to-one functions and so do not have inverses.

However, we can specify new functions with the same rules as these functions, but with smaller domains, to ensure that the new functions are one-to-one and have the same image sets as the original functions. These new functions then have inverses, as defined in the box below.

### Inverse trigonometric functions

The **inverse sine function** $\sin^{-1}$ is the function with domain $[-1, 1]$ and rule

$$\sin^{-1} x = y,$$

where $y$ is the number in the interval $\left[-\dfrac{\pi}{2}, \dfrac{\pi}{2}\right]$ such that $\sin y = x$.

The **inverse cosine function** $\cos^{-1}$ is the function with domain $[-1, 1]$ and rule

$$\cos^{-1} x = y,$$

where $y$ is the number in the interval $[0, \pi]$ such that $\cos y = x$.

The **inverse tangent function** $\tan^{-1}$ is the function with domain $\mathbb{R}$ and rule

$$\tan^{-1} x = y,$$

where $y$ is the number in the interval $\left(-\dfrac{\pi}{2}, \dfrac{\pi}{2}\right)$ such that $\tan y = x$.

Equations that include trigonometric functions are known as **trigonometric equations**. The inverse trigonometric functions can be used with the ASTC diagram to solve these trigonometric equations.

**Example 3**   *Solving simple trigonometric equations using the ASTC diagram and inverse trigonometric functions*

Find all solutions between $-\pi$ and $\pi$ of the equation $\cos \theta = -\frac{1}{2}$. Give exact answers.

**Solution**

🔍 Use the ASTC diagram to find the possible quadrants where the solutions lie. 💬

The cosine of $\theta$ is negative so, from the ASTC diagram, $\theta$ must be a second- or third-quadrant angle.

🔍 For the two possible quadrants, draw a sketch showing the angle $\theta$ and the line $OP$ from the origin $O$ to the point $P$ on the unit circle corresponding to $\theta$. On each sketch, mark the acute angle $\phi$ between $OP$ and the $x$-axis. 💬

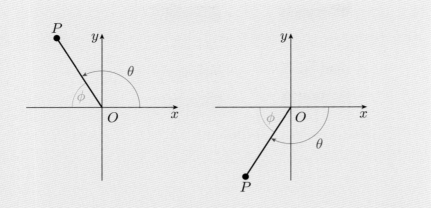

🔍 Use the given equation to write down the value of $\cos\phi$. Then use the special angles table to find $\phi$. 💭

Here

$$\cos\theta = -\tfrac{1}{2},$$

so

$$\cos\phi = \tfrac{1}{2},$$

and hence

$$\phi = \cos^{-1}\left(\tfrac{1}{2}\right) = \frac{\pi}{3}.$$

🔍 Now use your sketches to find the possible values of $\theta$. 💭

The solutions are

$$\theta = \pi - \phi = \pi - \frac{\pi}{3} = \frac{2\pi}{3}$$

and

$$\theta = -(\pi - \phi) = -\frac{2\pi}{3}.$$

---

In the previous example, it was easiest to use the special angles table to work out the value of the inverse cosine function because an exact value was required. However, you can also use the inverse trigonometric function keys on your calculator, especially where a decimal approximation to the angle is sufficient. If you do use your calculator, remember to check that the mode of the calculator is set to degrees or radians as appropriate before you start.

> **Activity 12**    *Solving trigonometric equations using the ASTC diagram and inverse trigonometric functions*
>
> (a)  Find all solutions between $0$ and $2\pi$ of the equation $\tan\theta = -\dfrac{1}{\sqrt{3}}$.
>
>       Give exact answers.
>
> (b)  Find all solutions between $-180°$ and $180°$ of the equation $\sin\theta = -0.8$. Give your answers to the nearest degree.

The next example shows how you can use a graph to solve a trigonometric equation.

---

**Example 4**    *Solving trigonometric equations using a graph*

Find all solutions between $0$ and $2\pi$ of the equation $\cos\theta = -\dfrac{\sqrt{3}}{2}$. Give exact answers.

**Solution**

🗨 Sketch the graph of the cosine function in the interval $0$ to $2\pi$.

Sketch the horizontal line at height $-\dfrac{\sqrt{3}}{2}$, and mark the crossing points. The $\theta$-coordinates of these points are the required solutions of $\cos\theta = -\dfrac{\sqrt{3}}{2}$. 🗨

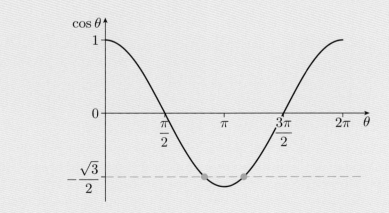

🗨 Find one solution using the inverse cosine function. 🗨

One solution (the solution in the interval $[0, \pi]$) is

$$\theta = \cos^{-1}\left(-\frac{\sqrt{3}}{2}\right) = \frac{5\pi}{6}.$$

🔍 Use the symmetry of the graph to find the other solution. 💬

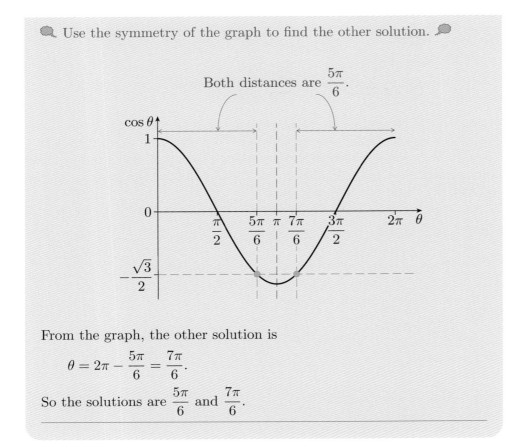

Both distances are $\dfrac{5\pi}{6}$.

From the graph, the other solution is

$$\theta = 2\pi - \frac{5\pi}{6} = \frac{7\pi}{6}.$$

So the solutions are $\dfrac{5\pi}{6}$ and $\dfrac{7\pi}{6}$.

---

**Activity 13**  *Solving trigonometric equations using a graph*

(a) Use a graph to find all solutions between $-180°$ and $180°$ of the equation $\sin\theta = 0.2$. Give your answers to the nearest degree.

(b) Use a graph to find all solutions between $-\pi$ and $\pi$ of the equation $\tan\theta = -3$. Give your answers to three significant figures.

## 2.2  Trigonometric identities

> For more detail on the topics covered in this subsection, refer to Section 4 of MST124 Unit 4.

A **trigonometric identity** is an equation that involves one or more trigonometric expressions and which is satisfied by all values of the variables for which the expressions are defined.

For example,

$$\tan \theta = \frac{\sin \theta}{\cos \theta}$$

is a trigonometric identity that is true for *any* angle $\theta$, provided that $\cos \theta \neq 0$.

Trigonometric identities can involve the sine, cosine and tangent functions and their reciprocal functions, namely the cosecant, secant and cotangent. These functions are defined in the box below. Note that the names of these functions are often abbreviated to cosec, sec and cot respectively (pronounced 'co-seck', 'seck' and 'cot').

---

**Cosecant, secant and cotangent**

$$\operatorname{cosec} \theta = \frac{1}{\sin \theta} \quad (\text{provided } \sin \theta \neq 0)$$

$$\sec \theta = \frac{1}{\cos \theta} \quad (\text{provided } \cos \theta \neq 0)$$

$$\cot \theta = \frac{\cos \theta}{\sin \theta} \quad (\text{provided } \sin \theta \neq 0)$$

---

Since you have already seen that

$$\tan \theta = \frac{\sin \theta}{\cos \theta} \quad (\text{provided } \cos \theta \neq 0),$$

it follows from the third equation in the box above that

$$\cot \theta = \frac{1}{\tan \theta} \quad (\text{provided } \sin \theta \neq 0 \text{ and } \cos \theta \neq 0).$$

**Activity 14**   *Finding values of cosecant, secant and cotangent*

(a) Using the special angles table, calculate the values of $\operatorname{cosec} \theta$, $\sec \theta$ and $\cot \theta$ for $\theta$ equal to $\pi/3$. Give exact answers.

(b) For which values of $\theta$ is the function $g(\theta) = \operatorname{cosec}(2\theta)$ *not* defined?

There is a list of useful trigonometric identities in the *Quick reference material* in the *Handbook*.

The following two trigonometric identities (the first was already stated above) are used so frequently that they are worth memorising:

$$\tan \theta = \frac{\sin \theta}{\cos \theta}, \quad \sin^2 \theta + \cos^2 \theta = 1.$$

Sometimes, instead of looking up a trigonometric identity, it is just as quick to derive it from an identity that you know, as illustrated in the next activity.

**Activity 15**    *Deriving trigonometric identities*

(a) By starting with the identity $\sin^2\theta + \cos^2\theta = 1$ and dividing through by $\cos^2\theta$, derive the identity

$$\tan^2\theta + 1 = \sec^2\theta.$$

(b) Use a similar method to derive the identity

$$1 + \cot^2\theta = \operatorname{cosec}^2\theta.$$

**Activity 16**    *Using identities to calculate trigonometric values*

Suppose that $\phi$ is an acute angle and that $\cos\phi = \frac{1}{2}$. Use a trigonometric identity from the *Quick reference material* in the *Handbook* to find the exact value for $\cos(2\phi)$.

# 3  Vectors

This section summarises the key ideas about vectors that are explained more fully in MST124 Unit 5. It assumes that you are familiar with using the sine and cosine rules to determine unknown side lengths and angles in triangles. These rules are summarised in the box below. If you are not confident with this topic, then you should work through Section 3 of MST124 Unit 4 before studying this section.

---

**The sine and cosine rules**

The rules below apply for a triangle with angles $A$, $B$ and $C$ and sides $a$, $b$ and $c$ (see Figure 20).

**Sine rule**

$$\frac{a}{\sin A} = \frac{b}{\sin B} = \frac{c}{\sin C}$$

**Cosine rule**

$$a^2 = b^2 + c^2 - 2bc\cos A$$
$$b^2 = c^2 + a^2 - 2ca\cos B$$
$$c^2 = a^2 + b^2 - 2ab\cos C$$

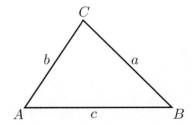

**Figure 20**    A triangle with angles $A$, $B$ and $C$ and sides $a$, $b$ and $c$

---

Try the following quiz to determine which topics in this section you need to revise thoroughly.

**Activity 17**  *Vectors quiz*

In this activity, **i**, **j** and **k** are unit vectors in the direction of the positive $x$-, $y$- and $z$-axes respectively.

(a) A hiker walks 4 km on a bearing of 210°, then 7 km on a bearing of 290°. What is the distance and bearing of the hiker's final position from her starting point? Give the distance to two significant figures and the bearing to the nearest degree.

(b) Express each of the following vectors in component form and hence find their magnitude and direction.

    (i)   $\mathbf{a} + 2\mathbf{b} - 0.5\mathbf{c}$, where $\mathbf{a} = \mathbf{i} - \mathbf{j}$, $\mathbf{b} = -2\mathbf{i} + \mathbf{j}$ and $\mathbf{c} = 6\mathbf{i} - 4\mathbf{j}$.

        Give the magnitude to two significant figures, and the direction as a bearing to the nearest degree.

    (ii)  $2\begin{pmatrix} -3 \\ 4 \end{pmatrix} - \begin{pmatrix} 2 \\ 5 \end{pmatrix} + 3\begin{pmatrix} 0 \\ -2 \end{pmatrix}$.

        Give the magnitude to two significant figures, and the direction as the angle this vector makes with the positive $x$-axis, to the nearest degree.

(c) A vector **p** has magnitude 5 and makes an angle of $-130°$ with the positive $x$-axis. Express **p** in component form, giving each component to three significant figures.

(d) Find, to the nearest degree, the angle between the vectors

    $\mathbf{p} = 2\mathbf{i} - 3\mathbf{j} + \mathbf{k}$ and $\mathbf{q} = 3\mathbf{i} - 2\mathbf{j}$.

## 3.1  Vectors and scalars

> For more detail on the topics covered in this subsection, refer to Section 5 of MST124 Unit 5.

In general, **displacement** is the position of one point relative to another, whether in one, two or three dimensions. To specify the displacement of an object, you must give both its distance away from the reference point and the direction from the reference point to the object.

Just as distance together with direction is called displacement, so speed together with direction is called **velocity**. To specify the velocity of an object, you need to give both its speed and its direction of travel, for example, $20 \, \text{m s}^{-1}$ in a north-east direction.

Velocity has both magnitude and direction

Quantities such as displacement and velocity that have both a size and a direction are called **vectors**. Vectors are often denoted by lower-case letters. To distinguish vectors from other quantities, the letters are written in bold typeface in printed materials, for example, $\mathbf{v}$, and they are underlined when handwritten, for example, $\underline{v}$.

The size of a vector is usually called its **magnitude**. The magnitude of an object's velocity is its speed, for example, $20\,\mathrm{m\,s^{-1}}$. The magnitude of a vector $\mathbf{v}$ is denoted by $|\mathbf{v}|$. So, if $\mathbf{v}$ represents the object's velocity, then $|\mathbf{v}| = 20\,\mathrm{m\,s^{-1}}$.

Quantities which only have a magnitude and do not have a direction are known as **scalars**. For example, speed is a scalar quantity; it is the magnitude of velocity.

In practical problems, the direction of a vector may be given as a bearing.

> A **bearing** is an angle between $0°$ and $360°$, measured clockwise from north to the direction of interest.

Using a map and compass to take a bearing

For example, if a town is south-west of a village, the bearing of the town from the village is $225°$, as shown in Figure 21. The bearing of the village from the town is $45°$.

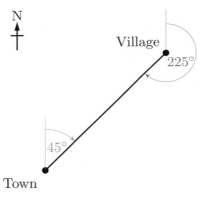

**Figure 21** The bearings of the town and the village from each other

A vector can be represented by an arrow. The length of the arrow represents the magnitude of the vector and the direction of the arrow represents the direction of the vector. For example, using a scale in which $1\,\mathrm{cm}$ represents $10\,\mathrm{m\,s^{-1}}$, the velocity $\mathbf{v}$ of a car that is travelling at $20\,\mathrm{m\,s^{-1}}$ in a north-east direction, can be represented by an arrow that is $2\,\mathrm{cm}$ long and that makes an angle of $45°$ with a line indicating the north direction, as shown in Figure 22(a). Note that any arrow of length $2\,\mathrm{cm}$ and pointing in a north-east direction can be used to represent $\mathbf{v}$.

A displacement vector from the point $P$ to the point $Q$ is usually (but not always) denoted by $\overrightarrow{PQ}$ and is represented by an arrow which joins

$P$ to $Q$, as shown in Figure 22(b). The magnitude of the displacement vector $\overrightarrow{PQ}$ is usually written $PQ$, which is the usual notation for the distance between two points on a line. So $|\overrightarrow{PQ}| = PQ$.

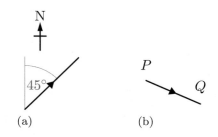

**Figure 22**   Arrows that represent vectors

Two vectors are equal if they have the same magnitude and the same direction.

The **zero vector**, **0**, has zero magnitude and no direction. A **unit vector** is a vector whose magnitude is 1.

Two vectors can be added together, either by using the triangle rule or the parallelogram rule, whichever is more convenient. These rules are summarised in the boxes below. The sum of two vectors is also called their **resultant**.

### Triangle law for vector addition

To find the sum of two vectors **a** and **b**, place the tail of **b** at the tip of **a**. Then **a** + **b** is the vector from the tail of **a** to the tip of **b**.

### Parallelogram law for vector addition

To find the sum of two vectors **a** and **b**, place their tails together, and complete the resulting figure to form a parallelogram. Then **a** + **b** is the vector formed by the diagonal of the parallelogram, starting from the point where the tails of **a** and **b** meet.

You can add more than two vectors together. To add several vectors, you place them all tip to tail, one after another; their sum is then the vector from the tail of the first vector to the tip of the last vector. The order in which you add vectors does not matter – you always get the same resultant.

The following example indicates how to find the resultant of two vectors in a practical setting. When a boat sails in a current its actual velocity is the resultant of the velocity it would have in still water and the velocity of the current. In particular, the direction in which the boat is pointing – this is called its **heading**, when it is given as a bearing – may be different from the direction in which it is actually moving, which is called its **course**.

---

**Example 5**   *Adding vectors*

A boat has a speed in still water of $5\,\text{m}\,\text{s}^{-1}$ and is sailing on a heading of $25°$. However, there is a current in the water of speed $3\,\text{m}\,\text{s}^{-1}$ flowing on a bearing of $120°$. Find the resultant velocity of the boat, in terms of its speed in $\text{m}\,\text{s}^{-1}$ (to one decimal place) and its course, given as a bearing (to the nearest degree).

**Solution**

🔍 Draw a diagram showing the vectors. 💬

Let **b** be the velocity of the boat in still water and **c** be the velocity of the current. The resultant velocity of the boat is **b** + **c**, as shown below.

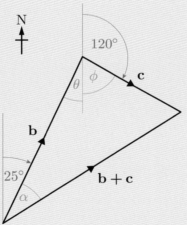

🔍 Mark known lengths and angles in the triangle. 💬

We know that $|\mathbf{b}| = 5$ and $|\mathbf{c}| = 3$.

Since alternate angles are equal, the angle $\theta$ marked at the tip of **b** is $25°$.

The angle $\phi$ marked at the tail of **c** is given by $\phi = 180° - 120° = 60°$.

So the top angle of the triangle is $\theta + \phi = 25° + 60° = 85°$.

🔍 Use the cosine rule to find the magnitude of the resultant vector. 💬

Applying the cosine rule gives

$$|\mathbf{b} + \mathbf{c}|^2 = |\mathbf{b}|^2 + |\mathbf{c}|^2 - 2|\mathbf{b}||\mathbf{c}|\cos(\theta + \phi),$$

so

$$|\mathbf{b} + \mathbf{c}| = \sqrt{5^2 + 3^2 - 2 \times 5 \times 3 \times \cos 85°}$$
$$= 5.602\ldots.$$

🔍 Use the sine rule to find the unknown angle $\alpha$. 💬

The angle $\alpha$ can be found by using the sine rule:

$$\frac{|\mathbf{c}|}{\sin\alpha} = \frac{|\mathbf{b} + \mathbf{c}|}{\sin(\theta + \phi)}$$

$$\sin\alpha = \frac{|\mathbf{c}|\sin(\theta + \phi)}{|\mathbf{b} + \mathbf{c}|} = \frac{3\sin 85°}{5.602\ldots}.$$

Now,

$$\sin^{-1}\left(\frac{3\sin 85°}{5.602\ldots}\right) = 32.239\ldots°.$$

So $\alpha = 32.239\ldots°$ or $\alpha = 180° - 32.239\ldots° = 147.760\ldots°$.

But $|\mathbf{c}| < |\mathbf{b} + \mathbf{c}|$, so we expect $\alpha < \theta + \phi$; that is, $\alpha < 85°$. So $\alpha = 32.239\ldots°$ and hence the bearing of $\mathbf{b} + \mathbf{c}$ is

$$25° + 32.239\ldots° = 57.239\ldots°.$$

The resultant velocity of the boat is therefore $5.6\,\mathrm{m\,s^{-1}}$ (to 1 d.p.) on a bearing of $57°$ (to the nearest degree).

---

## Activity 18  *Adding vectors*

The displacement from Milton Keynes to Nottingham is 109 km with a bearing of 342°, and the displacement from Nottingham to Birmingham is 75 km with a bearing of 222°. Find the magnitude (to the nearest kilometre) and direction (as a bearing, to the nearest degree) of the displacement from Milton Keynes to Birmingham.

The *negative* of a vector **a** is denoted by −**a**, and is defined as follows.

### Negative of a vector

The **negative** of a vector **a**, denoted by −**a**, is the vector with the same magnitude as **a**, but the opposite direction.

For any points $P$ and $Q$, $\overrightarrow{PQ} = -\overrightarrow{QP}$, since $\overrightarrow{PQ}$ and $\overrightarrow{QP}$ have the same magnitude but opposite directions.

The idea of the negative of a vector is used to define vector subtraction, as in the box below.

### Vector subtraction

To subtract **b** from **a**, add −**b** to **a**. That is,

$$\mathbf{a} - \mathbf{b} = \mathbf{a} + (-\mathbf{b}).$$

If you multiply a vector by a positive scalar, then the new vector has the same direction as the original vector, but its magnitude is multiplied by the scalar. For example, the vector 2**a** has a magnitude double that of **a** and the same direction. It is represented by an arrow parallel to and double the length of the arrow that represents **a**.

### Scalar multiple of a vector

Suppose that **a** is a vector. Then, for any non-zero real number $m$, the **scalar multiple** $m\mathbf{a}$ of **a** is the vector

- whose magnitude is $|m|$ times the magnitude of **a**
- that has the same direction as **a** if $m$ is positive, and the opposite direction if $m$ is negative.

Also, $0\mathbf{a} = \mathbf{0}$.
(That is, the number zero times the vector **a** is the zero vector.)

**Activity 19** *Adding and subtracting vectors*

The diagram below shows two vectors **u** and **v** drawn on a grid.

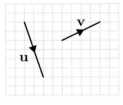

Draw arrows representing the following vectors. You might find it useful to use squared paper.

(a) $\frac{1}{2}\mathbf{u}$    (b) $-2\mathbf{v}$    (c) $\frac{1}{2}\mathbf{u} - 2\mathbf{v}$

The box below summarises the basic algebraic properties of vectors. Using these properties, you can perform some operations on vector expressions that are similar to the operations you can perform on real numbers.

**Properties of vector algebra**

The following properties hold for all vectors **a**, **b** and **c**, and all scalars $m$ and $n$.

1.  $\mathbf{a} + \mathbf{b} = \mathbf{b} + \mathbf{a}$
2.  $(\mathbf{a} + \mathbf{b}) + \mathbf{c} = \mathbf{a} + (\mathbf{b} + \mathbf{c})$
3.  $\mathbf{a} + \mathbf{0} = \mathbf{a}$
4.  $\mathbf{a} + (-\mathbf{a}) = \mathbf{0}$
5.  $m(\mathbf{a} + \mathbf{b}) = m\mathbf{a} + m\mathbf{b}$
6.  $(m + n)\mathbf{a} = m\mathbf{a} + n\mathbf{a}$
7.  $m(n\mathbf{a}) = (mn)\mathbf{a}$
8.  $1\mathbf{a} = \mathbf{a}$

**Example 6** *Manipulating vector expressions and equations*

(a) Simplify the vector expression

$$3(\mathbf{a} - 2\mathbf{b}) - 4(2\mathbf{b} + \mathbf{c}) + 2(3\mathbf{a} + 2\mathbf{b} - 4\mathbf{c}).$$

(b) Rearrange the following equation to express **x** in terms of **a** and **b**.

$$3(\mathbf{b} - \mathbf{a}) + \mathbf{x} = 5\mathbf{a} + 2(\mathbf{x} - \mathbf{b}).$$

**Solution**

(a) 🔍 Expand the brackets, using property 5 above. 💬

$$3(\mathbf{a} - 2\mathbf{b}) - 4(2\mathbf{b} + \mathbf{c}) + 2(3\mathbf{a} + 2\mathbf{b} - 4\mathbf{c})$$
$$= 3\mathbf{a} - 6\mathbf{b} - 8\mathbf{b} - 4\mathbf{c} + 6\mathbf{a} + 4\mathbf{b} - 8\mathbf{c}$$
$$= 9\mathbf{a} - 10\mathbf{b} - 12\mathbf{c}.$$

(b) 🔍 First expand the brackets, using property 5 above. 💬

$$3(\mathbf{b} - \mathbf{a}) + \mathbf{x} = 5\mathbf{a} + 2(\mathbf{x} - \mathbf{b})$$
$$3\mathbf{b} - 3\mathbf{a} + \mathbf{x} = 5\mathbf{a} + 2\mathbf{x} - 2\mathbf{b}$$

🔍 Then collect like terms and simplify. 💬

$$5\mathbf{b} - 8\mathbf{a} = \mathbf{x}$$

So,

$$\mathbf{x} = 5\mathbf{b} - 8\mathbf{a}.$$

---

**Activity 20**    *Manipulating vector expressions and equations*

(a) Simplify the vector expression $2(\mathbf{a} - \mathbf{b}) - 4(\mathbf{c} - \mathbf{b}) + 3(\mathbf{a} - 2\mathbf{b} + 3\mathbf{c})$.

(b) Rearrange each of the following vector equations to express $\mathbf{x}$ in terms of $\mathbf{a}$, $\mathbf{b}$ and $\mathbf{c}$.

    (i) $3\mathbf{a} + 2\mathbf{x} = 4\mathbf{a} - \mathbf{c}$      (ii) $3\mathbf{x} - 2(\mathbf{b} - 2\mathbf{c}) = 4(\mathbf{a} + \mathbf{b}) + 3(\mathbf{b} - 2\mathbf{x})$

## 3.2  Component form of a vector

> For more detail on the topics covered in this subsection, refer to Section 6 of MST124 Unit 5.

In the previous subsection, you saw how to specify a vector in terms of its magnitude and direction. In this subsection, you'll see how to specify a vector in terms of its components along mutually perpendicular coordinate axes. This representation is known as the **component form** of the vector.

The first step in representing a two-dimensional vector in component form is to choose two perpendicular coordinate axes, and label them as the $x$- and $y$-axes. Next, define $\mathbf{i}$ and $\mathbf{j}$ as unit vectors in the directions of the positive $x$- and $y$-axes. Then any two-dimensional vector can be written as the sum of scalar multiples of $\mathbf{i}$ and $\mathbf{j}$. For example, the two-dimensional vector $\mathbf{v}$ shown in Figure 23(a) can be written in component form as $\mathbf{v} = a\mathbf{i} + b\mathbf{j}$.

A three-dimensional vector can be represented in component form by adding a third axis, labelled as the $z$-axis, perpendicular to both the $x$- and the $y$-axes, and defining $\mathbf{k}$ as a unit vector in the direction of the positive $z$-axis. Then any three-dimensional vector can be written as the sum of scalar multiples of $\mathbf{i}$, $\mathbf{j}$ and $\mathbf{k}$. For example, the three-dimensional vector $\mathbf{v}$ shown in Figure 23(b) can be written in component form as $\mathbf{v} = a\mathbf{i} + b\mathbf{j} + c\mathbf{k}$.

The scalars $a, b$ and $c$ are either called the **i**-component, **j**-component and **k**-component of $\mathbf{v}$, or the $x$-component, $y$-component and $z$-component of $\mathbf{v}$, respectively.

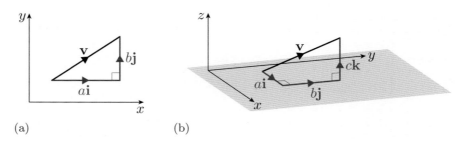

(a)    (b)

**Figure 23**   Vectors expressed as sums of scalar multiples of Cartesian unit vectors

It is particularly simple to express the **position vector** of a point in component form. If $P$ is any point, either in the coordinate plane or in three-dimensional space, then the *position vector* of $P$ is the displacement vector $\overrightarrow{OP}$, where $O$ is the origin. The components of a position vector are the same as the coordinates of the point.

This is illustrated in Figure 24, in the case of two dimensions. Thus the position vector of $P$ is $\overrightarrow{OP} = x\mathbf{i} + y\mathbf{j}$.

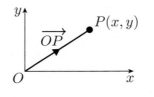

**Figure 24**   The position vector $\overrightarrow{OP}$ in two dimensions

Similarly, if a point $P$ in three-dimensional space has coordinates $(x, y, z)$, then its position vector $\overrightarrow{OP} = x\mathbf{i} + y\mathbf{j} + z\mathbf{k}$.

An alternative notation for expressing a vector in component form is to write it as a column vector. For example, the vector $\mathbf{v} = a\mathbf{i} + b\mathbf{j} + c\mathbf{k}$ in Figure 23(b) can also be denoted by the column vector

$$\mathbf{v} = \begin{pmatrix} a \\ b \\ c \end{pmatrix}.$$

You can use whichever notation is most convenient.

All the usual properties of vector algebra that you saw in the previous subsection apply to vectors in component form. In particular, they can be added, subtracted and multiplied by scalars.

For example, if $\mathbf{p} = 2\mathbf{i} - \mathbf{j} + 3\mathbf{k}$ and $\mathbf{q} = -3\mathbf{i} + 2\mathbf{j} - \mathbf{k}$, then

$$
\begin{aligned}
4\mathbf{p} - 3\mathbf{q} &= 4(2\mathbf{i} - \mathbf{j} + 3\mathbf{k}) - 3(-3\mathbf{i} + 2\mathbf{j} - \mathbf{k}) \\
&= 8\mathbf{i} - 4\mathbf{j} + 12\mathbf{k} + 9\mathbf{i} - 6\mathbf{j} + 3\mathbf{k} \\
&= 17\mathbf{i} - 10\mathbf{j} + 15\mathbf{k}.
\end{aligned}
$$

**Activity 21**  *Simplifying combinations of vectors in component form*

Find each of the following vectors in component form.

(a)  $2\mathbf{p} - \mathbf{q} - 3\mathbf{r}$, where $\mathbf{p} = 3\mathbf{i} - 2\mathbf{j}$, $\mathbf{q} = 2\mathbf{i} + \mathbf{j}$ and $\mathbf{r} = -2\mathbf{i} + 3\mathbf{j}$

(b)  $3 \begin{pmatrix} 1 \\ -2 \end{pmatrix} + 2 \begin{pmatrix} -1 \\ 2 \end{pmatrix} - 2 \begin{pmatrix} 2 \\ 5 \end{pmatrix}$

(c)  $0.5\mathbf{e} + 1.5\mathbf{f}$, where $\mathbf{e} = 3\mathbf{i} - 2\mathbf{j} + \mathbf{k}$ and $\mathbf{f} = 3\mathbf{i} - 4\mathbf{j} - 2\mathbf{k}$

(d)  $a \begin{pmatrix} 2 \\ -3 \\ 1 \end{pmatrix} + 4 \begin{pmatrix} -a \\ a \\ -2a \end{pmatrix} - 3a \begin{pmatrix} -1 \\ 2 \\ -3 \end{pmatrix}$, where $a$ is any real number

If a vector is expressed in component form, you can find its magnitude from its components. For example, referring back to Figure 23, the magnitude of the two-dimensional vector $\mathbf{v} = a\mathbf{i} + b\mathbf{j}$ is given by

$$|\mathbf{v}| = \sqrt{a^2 + b^2},$$

and the magnitude of the three-dimensional vector $\mathbf{v} = a\mathbf{i} + b\mathbf{j} + c\mathbf{k}$ is given by

$$|\mathbf{v}| = \sqrt{a^2 + b^2 + c^2}.$$

You can also calculate the direction of a two-dimensional vector from its components. The method is illustrated in the following example. Remember that the direction of a two-dimensional vector can be given either as a bearing, or as an angle measured in an *anticlockwise* direction from the positive $x$-direction to the direction of the vector (though sometimes it is helpful to use negative angles to denote angles measured clockwise from the positive $x$-direction).

Techniques involving the directions of three-dimensional vectors are more complicated and are not covered here.

**Example 7**   *Finding the magnitude and direction of a two-dimensional vector from its components*

Find the magnitude of the vector $-8\mathbf{i} + 15\mathbf{j}$, and the angle that it makes with the positive $x$-direction. Give the exact value of the magnitude, and the angle to the nearest degree.

**Solution**

🗨 Use the standard formula to find the magnitude. 🗨

The magnitude of the vector is
$$\sqrt{(-8)^2 + 15^2} = \sqrt{64 + 225} = \sqrt{289} = 17.$$

🗨 To find the required angle, first draw a diagram. 🗨

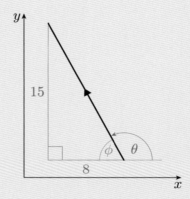

🗨 Find the acute angle $\phi$, and hence find the required angle $\theta$. 🗨

From the diagram,
$$\tan\phi = \frac{15}{8},$$
so
$$\phi = \tan^{-1}\left(\frac{15}{8}\right) = 61.92\ldots^{\circ}.$$

Hence the angle that the vector makes with the positive $x$-direction, labelled $\theta$ in the diagram, is
$$180^{\circ} - 61.92\ldots^{\circ} = 118.07\ldots^{\circ}$$
$$= 118^{\circ} \text{ (to the nearest degree).}$$

**Activity 22**   *Finding the magnitudes and directions of vectors from their components*

(a) Find the magnitudes of the following vectors, and calculate the angle in degrees that each vector makes with the positive $x$-direction. Give answers to one decimal place.

(i)  $3\mathbf{i} - \mathbf{j}$      (ii)  $\begin{pmatrix} -2 \\ -3 \end{pmatrix}$

(b) Find the magnitudes of the following three-dimensional vectors. Give exact answers.

(i)  $-\mathbf{i} + 2\mathbf{j} - 4\mathbf{k}$      (ii)  $\begin{pmatrix} -2 \\ -1 \\ \sqrt{3} \end{pmatrix}$

If you know the magnitude and direction of a two-dimensional vector, you can convert it into component form. Figure 25 shows a vector $\mathbf{v}$ that makes an acute angle $\theta$ with the positive $x$-direction. From the diagram, the component form is

$$\mathbf{v} = |\mathbf{v}| \cos \theta \, \mathbf{i} + |\mathbf{v}| \sin \theta \, \mathbf{j}.$$

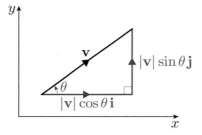

**Figure 25**   A vector $\mathbf{v}$ and its components

The same formula works for *any* angle $\theta$ measured from the positive $x$-direction, as summarised in the box below and illustrated in the next example.

**Component form of a two-dimensional vector in terms of its magnitude and its angle with the positive $x$-direction**

If the two-dimensional vector $\mathbf{v}$ makes the angle $\theta$ with the positive $x$-direction, then

$$\mathbf{v} = |\mathbf{v}| \cos \theta \, \mathbf{i} + |\mathbf{v}| \sin \theta \, \mathbf{j}.$$

**Example 8**    *Calculating the components of a vector from its magnitude and direction*

A vector $\mathbf{v}$ with magnitude 3 makes an angle of $330°$ with the positive $x$-direction. Express $\mathbf{v}$ in component form.

**Solution**

🔍 If $\mathbf{v}$ makes the angle $\theta$ with the positive $x$-direction, then $\mathbf{v} = |\mathbf{v}| \cos\theta\, \mathbf{i} + |\mathbf{v}| \sin\theta\, \mathbf{j}$. 💬

The component form of a vector $\mathbf{v}$ with magnitude 3 that makes an angle of $330°$ with the positive $x$-direction, is

$$
\begin{aligned}
\mathbf{v} &= 3\cos 330° \mathbf{i} + 3\sin 330° \mathbf{j} \\
&= 3\cos 30° \mathbf{i} - 3\sin 30° \mathbf{j} \\
&= 3 \times \frac{\sqrt{3}}{2}\mathbf{i} - 3 \times \frac{1}{2}\mathbf{j} \\
&= \frac{3\sqrt{3}}{2}\mathbf{i} - \frac{3}{2}\mathbf{j}.
\end{aligned}
$$

Here are some vectors for you to express in component form. Remember that if the direction of a vector is given as a bearing, then you need to start by finding the angle that the vector makes with the positive $x$-direction.

**Activity 23**    *Calculating the components of vectors from their magnitudes and directions*

Express the following vectors in component form, giving each component to two significant figures.

(a)  The vector $\mathbf{r}$ with magnitude 4.5 that makes an angle of $165°$ with the positive $x$-direction.

(b)  The velocity vector $\mathbf{w}$ with magnitude $5\,\mathrm{m\,s^{-1}}$ and bearing $190°$.

## 3.3  Scalar product

For more detail on the topics covered in this subsection, refer to Section 7 of MST124 Unit 5.

Two vectors can be multiplied together to form their **scalar product** (also known as their **dot product**), as described in the box below.

## Scalar product of two vectors

The **scalar product** of the non-zero vectors **a** and **b** is

$$\mathbf{a} \cdot \mathbf{b} = |\mathbf{a}|\,|\mathbf{b}|\cos\theta,$$

where $\theta$ is the angle between **a** and **b**.

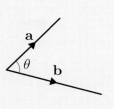

If **a** or **b** is the zero vector, then $\mathbf{a} \cdot \mathbf{b} = 0$.

The definition of scalar product applies to both two-dimensional and three-dimensional vectors.

Note that this method of multiplying two vectors together results in a *scalar* quantity, not a vector quantity, which is why it is called the scalar product.

## Activity 24   *Some properties of scalar products*

(a) Suppose that **a** and **b** are non-zero vectors. Show that the following statements are true.

   (i)   If **a** and **b** are perpendicular, then $\mathbf{a} \cdot \mathbf{b} = 0$, and vice-versa.

   (ii)  $\mathbf{a} \cdot \mathbf{b} = \mathbf{b} \cdot \mathbf{a}$.

(b) If **i**, **j** and **k** are unit vectors in the directions of the positive $x$-, $y$- and $z$-axes, then show that

$$\mathbf{i} \cdot \mathbf{j} = \mathbf{j} \cdot \mathbf{k} = \mathbf{k} \cdot \mathbf{i} = 0 \quad \text{and} \quad \mathbf{i} \cdot \mathbf{i} = \mathbf{j} \cdot \mathbf{j} = \mathbf{k} \cdot \mathbf{k} = 1.$$

The definition of the scalar product can be used to show that

$$\mathbf{a} \cdot (\mathbf{b} + \mathbf{c}) = \mathbf{a} \cdot \mathbf{b} + \mathbf{a} \cdot \mathbf{c} \quad \text{and} \quad (\mathbf{b} + \mathbf{c}) \cdot \mathbf{a} = \mathbf{b} \cdot \mathbf{a} + \mathbf{c} \cdot \mathbf{a}.$$

This is expressed by saying that the operation of taking a scalar product is distributive over vector addition.

This property of the scalar product can be used to show that, if two vectors are given in component form, then their scalar product can be calculated as in the box below.

## Scalar product of vectors in terms of components

If $\mathbf{a} = a_1\mathbf{i} + a_2\mathbf{j} + a_3\mathbf{k}$ and $\mathbf{b} = b_1\mathbf{i} + b_2\mathbf{j} + b_3\mathbf{k}$, then

$$\mathbf{a} \cdot \mathbf{b} = a_1 b_1 + a_2 b_2 + a_3 b_3.$$

In column notation,

$$\text{if } \mathbf{a} = \begin{pmatrix} a_1 \\ a_2 \\ a_3 \end{pmatrix} \text{ and } \mathbf{b} = \begin{pmatrix} b_1 \\ b_2 \\ b_3 \end{pmatrix}, \text{ then } \mathbf{a} \cdot \mathbf{b} = a_1 b_1 + a_2 b_2 + a_3 b_3.$$

Note that this method of calculating the scalar product of two vectors in component form applies equally to two-dimensional and three-dimensional vectors. The next example illustrates the method for two-dimensional vectors, and shows how the scalar product can be used to calculate the angle between two vectors.

**Example 9**  *Finding the scalar product of two vectors in component form and calculating the angle between them*

(a) Find the scalar product of the two vectors $\mathbf{a} = 3\mathbf{i} - 2\mathbf{j}$ and $\mathbf{b} = \mathbf{i} + 4\mathbf{j}$.

(b) Hence find the angle between the vectors $\mathbf{a}$ and $\mathbf{b}$, to the nearest degree.

**Solution**

(a) The scalar product is
$$\mathbf{a} \cdot \mathbf{b} = (3\mathbf{i} - 2\mathbf{j}) \cdot (\mathbf{i} + 4\mathbf{j}) = 3 \times 1 + (-2) \times 4 = -5.$$

(b) 🔍 Use the definition of the scalar product in terms of the magnitudes of $\mathbf{a}$ and $\mathbf{b}$ and the angle between them. 💬

The scalar product of $\mathbf{a}$ and $\mathbf{b}$ is defined as

$\mathbf{a} \cdot \mathbf{b} = |\mathbf{a}||\mathbf{b}| \cos\theta$, where $\theta$ is the angle between $\mathbf{a}$ and $\mathbf{b}$.

So, $\quad \cos\theta = \dfrac{\mathbf{a} \cdot \mathbf{b}}{|\mathbf{a}||\mathbf{b}|}$.

Now $|\mathbf{a}| = \sqrt{3^2 + (-2)^2} = \sqrt{13}$ and $|\mathbf{b}| = \sqrt{1^2 + 4^2} = \sqrt{17}$.

Since we know from part (a) that $\mathbf{a} \cdot \mathbf{b} = -5$, we have

$$\cos\theta = \frac{\mathbf{a} \cdot \mathbf{b}}{|\mathbf{a}||\mathbf{b}|} = \frac{-5}{\sqrt{13}\sqrt{17}} = -0.3363\ldots.$$

Hence, $\theta = \cos^{-1}(-0.3363\ldots) = 109.65\ldots° = 110°$, to the nearest degree.

**Activity 25**  *Calculating the angle between two vectors in component form*

Find, to the nearest degree, the angle between the vectors
$$\mathbf{a} = \mathbf{i} + 2\mathbf{j} - \mathbf{k} \quad \text{and} \quad \mathbf{b} = -2\mathbf{i} + \mathbf{j} + 2\mathbf{k}.$$

# 4 Matrices

This section summarises some of the key ideas about matrices that are explained more fully in MST124 Unit 9. Try the following quiz to determine which topics in this section you need to revise thoroughly.

---

**Activity 26**  *Matrices quiz*

Let $\mathbf{P} = \begin{pmatrix} 0.5 & 1 \\ 1 & 2 \end{pmatrix}$ $\qquad \mathbf{Q} = \begin{pmatrix} -2 & \frac{1}{4} \\ 3 & -1 \end{pmatrix}$ $\qquad$ and $\qquad \mathbf{R} = \begin{pmatrix} -1 \\ 3 \end{pmatrix}$.

(a) Calculate

    (i) $2\mathbf{P} - 3\mathbf{Q}$     (ii) $\mathbf{QR}$     (iii) $\mathbf{P}^2$     (iv) $\mathbf{Q}^{-1}$.

(b) Explain why it is not possible to calculate

    (i) $3\mathbf{P} + 2\mathbf{R}$     (ii) $\mathbf{R}^2$     (iii) $\mathbf{P}^{-1}$.

---

## 4.1 Matrix operations

> For more detail on the topics covered in this subsection, refer to Section 1 of MST124 Unit 9.

A **matrix** is a rectangular array of numbers, usually enclosed in brackets. Matrices have a great many applications, especially to problems involving large amounts of numerical data. They are used extensively in computer software, for example to represent large systems of equations or to transform objects in computer graphics.

Some examples of matrices are shown below.

$$\mathbf{A} = \begin{pmatrix} 2 & -3 \\ 4 & -1 \\ -2 & 0 \end{pmatrix} \qquad \mathbf{B} = \begin{pmatrix} 0.5 & -0.866 \\ 0.866 & 0.5 \end{pmatrix} \qquad \mathbf{C} = \begin{pmatrix} c_{11} & c_{12} & c_{13} \\ c_{21} & c_{22} & c_{23} \end{pmatrix}$$

The theory of electronic circuits is one of many areas where matrices are useful in physics

In printed material, matrices are usually represented by capital letters in bold typeface. When handwriting a matrix name, you just use a capital letter – there is no need to underline the letter (as you do for vectors). For example, the matrix $\mathbf{A}$ can be handwritten as A.

A matrix with $m$ rows and $n$ columns is known as an $m \times n$ matrix and its **size** is said to be $m \times n$. So, $\mathbf{A}$ has size $3 \times 2$, $\mathbf{B}$ has size $2 \times 2$ and $\mathbf{C}$ has size $2 \times 3$. If $m = n$, then the matrix is called a **square** matrix.

The entry in each row and column of a matrix is known as an **element** of the matrix. A matrix of size $m \times n$ contains $mn$ elements. For example, $\mathbf{A}$ contains six elements.

An element of a matrix is often denoted by a lower-case letter (usually the same letter as the matrix name), with the row and column numbers as a subscript. For example, $a_{21}$ denotes the element in the second row and first column of matrix $\mathbf{A}$, so $a_{21} = 4$. The elements of the matrix $\mathbf{C}$ above are all expressed in this form.

Two matrices are equal to each other if they are the same size and if corresponding elements are equal.

To add or subtract two matrices, they must be the same size. Then the sum (or difference) is obtained by adding (or subtracting) corresponding elements, as explained in the box below.

> **Adding and subtracting matrices**
>
> If $\mathbf{A}$ and $\mathbf{B}$ are $m \times n$ matrices, then $\mathbf{A} \pm \mathbf{B}$ is the $m \times n$ matrix where the element in row $i$ and column $j$ is $a_{ij} \pm b_{ij}$.
>
> The sum or difference of two matrices of different sizes is not defined.

To multiply a matrix by a number $k$, simply multiply each element of the matrix by $k$. The number $k$ is sometimes called the **scalar** $k$, to emphasise that it is a number and not a matrix.

> **Multiplying a matrix by a scalar**
>
> If $\mathbf{A}$ is an $m \times n$ matrix and $k$ is any real number, then $k\mathbf{A}$ is the matrix where the element in the $i$th row and $j$th column is $ka_{ij}$.

The next example illustrates adding scalar multiples of matrices together.

---

**Example 10**　*Adding together scalar multiples of matrices*

Let $\mathbf{P} = \begin{pmatrix} 1 & -2 \\ 4 & -6 \\ -\frac{1}{2} & 0 \end{pmatrix}$ and $\mathbf{Q} = \begin{pmatrix} 2 & 0 \\ -1 & -2 \\ 3 & 4 \end{pmatrix}$.

Calculate $4\mathbf{P} + 3\mathbf{Q}$.

**Solution**

🔍 Work out the multiples first: multiply each element of $\mathbf{P}$ by 4 and each element of $\mathbf{Q}$ by 3. Then add the matrices together. 💬

$$4P + 3Q = 4 \begin{pmatrix} 1 & -2 \\ 4 & -6 \\ -\frac{1}{2} & 0 \end{pmatrix} + 3 \begin{pmatrix} 2 & 0 \\ -1 & -2 \\ 3 & 4 \end{pmatrix}$$

$$= \begin{pmatrix} 4 & -8 \\ 16 & -24 \\ -2 & 0 \end{pmatrix} + \begin{pmatrix} 6 & 0 \\ -3 & -6 \\ 9 & 12 \end{pmatrix}$$

$$= \begin{pmatrix} 4 + 6 & -8 + 0 \\ 16 + (-3) & -24 + (-6) \\ -2 + 9 & 0 + 12 \end{pmatrix}$$

$$= \begin{pmatrix} 10 & -8 \\ 13 & -30 \\ 7 & 12 \end{pmatrix}.$$

Where a matrix has elements that are fractions, or that are numbers with a common factor, it is often neater to express the matrix as the product of a scalar factor and a matrix whose elements are integers.

For example,

$$\mathbf{E} = \begin{pmatrix} \frac{1}{3} & -\frac{1}{3} \\ \frac{2}{3} & -\frac{2}{3} \end{pmatrix} = \frac{1}{3} \begin{pmatrix} 1 & -1 \\ 2 & -2 \end{pmatrix} \quad \text{and} \quad \mathbf{F} = \begin{pmatrix} 12 & 8 \\ -4 & 16 \end{pmatrix} = 4 \begin{pmatrix} 3 & 2 \\ -1 & 4 \end{pmatrix}.$$

**Activity 27** *Adding and subtracting matrices and multiplying matrices by a scalar*

(a) Let $\mathbf{A} = \begin{pmatrix} 1 & -2 \\ 4 & -6 \end{pmatrix}$ and $\mathbf{B} = \begin{pmatrix} -2 & 3 \\ 1 & 0 \end{pmatrix}$.

Calculate $2\mathbf{A} - 3\mathbf{B}$.

(b) Simplify the following matrices by taking out a scalar factor.

(i) $\mathbf{C} = \begin{pmatrix} -10 & -15 \\ 0 & -5 \end{pmatrix}$ (ii) $\mathbf{D} = \begin{pmatrix} \frac{3}{2} & \frac{5}{2} \\ \frac{5}{2} & -\frac{1}{2} \end{pmatrix}$

Multiplying two matrices together is a more complicated process than either addition or scalar multiplication.

The general procedure is outlined in the box below.

**Matrix multiplication**

Let $\mathbf{A}$ and $\mathbf{B}$ be matrices. Then the product matrix $\mathbf{AB}$ can be formed only if the number of columns of $\mathbf{A}$ equals the number of rows of $\mathbf{B}$.

If $\mathbf{A}$ has size $m \times n$ and $\mathbf{B}$ has size $n \times p$, then the product $\mathbf{AB}$ has size $m \times p$.

The element in row $i$ and column $j$ of the product $\mathbf{AB}$ is obtained by multiplying each element in the $i$th row of $\mathbf{A}$ by the corresponding element in the $j$th column of $\mathbf{B}$ and adding the results.

In element notation, if $c_{ij}$ denotes the element in the $i$th row and $j$th column of $\mathbf{AB}$, then

$$c_{ij} = a_{i1}b_{1j} + a_{i2}b_{2j} + \ldots + a_{in}b_{nj}.$$

Figure 26 illustrates how row $i$ of a matrix $\mathbf{A}$ and column $j$ of a matrix $\mathbf{B}$ are combined to give the element in row $i$ and column $j$ of the product matrix $\mathbf{AB}$.

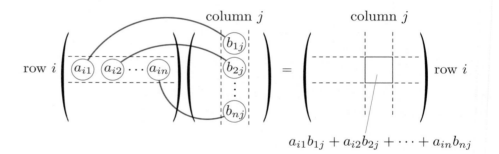

**Figure 26**   The element in row $i$ and column $j$ of a product matrix $\mathbf{AB}$ expressed in terms of elements from $\mathbf{A}$ and $\mathbf{B}$

You can quickly check whether two matrices can be multiplied together by writing down their sizes next to each other as follows.

$$m \times \boxed{n} \quad \text{times} \quad \boxed{p} \times q$$

The two matrices can be multiplied only if the two numbers in the boxes in the middle are equal, that is, if $n = p$. In this case, the size of the product matrix is given by the remaining numbers: the product of an $m \times n$ matrix and an $n \times q$ matrix has size $m \times q$.

For example, a $4 \times 2$ matrix can be multiplied by a $2 \times 3$ matrix, and the product has size $4 \times 3$.

**Example 11**   *Multiplying matrices*

Let $\mathbf{C} = \begin{pmatrix} 1 & -1 \\ -2 & 3 \\ 2 & 0 \end{pmatrix}$ and $\mathbf{D} = \begin{pmatrix} 0 & 1 \\ -1 & -2 \end{pmatrix}$.

Check that the product matrix $\mathbf{CD}$ can be formed, determine the size of $\mathbf{CD}$ and calculate it.

**Solution**

🔍 Write down the sizes of $\mathbf{C}$ and $\mathbf{D}$ and check if multiplication is possible. 💬

$\mathbf{C}$ has size $3 \times 2$ and $\mathbf{D}$ has size $2 \times 2$.

$$3 \times \boxed{2} \quad \boxed{2} \times 2$$

The numbers in the middle are equal, so the number of columns of $\mathbf{C}$ equals the number of rows of $\mathbf{D}$ and therefore $\mathbf{C}$ and $\mathbf{D}$ can be multiplied together to give $\mathbf{CD}$. The product has size $3 \times 2$.

🔍 To obtain the element in the $i$th row and the $j$th column of $\mathbf{CD}$, multiply each element in the $i$th row of $\mathbf{C}$ by the corresponding element in the $j$th column of $\mathbf{D}$, and add the results. 💬

$$\begin{pmatrix} 1 & -1 \\ -2 & 3 \\ 2 & 0 \end{pmatrix} \begin{pmatrix} 0 & 1 \\ -1 & -2 \end{pmatrix} = \begin{pmatrix} 1 \times 0 + (-1) \times (-1) & 1 \times 1 + (-1) \times (-2) \\ (-2) \times 0 + 3 \times (-1) & (-2) \times 1 + 3 \times (-2) \\ 2 \times 0 + 0 \times (-1) & 2 \times 1 + 0 \times (-2) \end{pmatrix}$$

$$= \begin{pmatrix} 1 & 3 \\ -3 & -8 \\ 0 & 2 \end{pmatrix}.$$

**Activity 28**   *Multiplying matrices*

Let $\mathbf{P} = \begin{pmatrix} 2 & -3 \\ 4 & -1 \\ -2 & 1 \end{pmatrix}$ $\quad \mathbf{Q} = \begin{pmatrix} -3 & 2 \\ 1 & 4 \end{pmatrix}$ and $\mathbf{R} = \begin{pmatrix} 2 \\ 1 \end{pmatrix}$.

(a) Calculate $\mathbf{PR}$.

(b) Explain why it is not possible to calculate $\mathbf{RP}$.

(c) Calculate $\mathbf{Q}^2$.

(d) The matrix $\mathbf{M}$ has size $m \times n$ where $m \neq n$. Explain why it is not possible to calculate $\mathbf{M}^2$.

The properties of matrix addition and scalar multiplication, and of matrix multiplication, are summarised in the MST125 *Handbook*, and you should remind yourself of them.

It is particularly important to remember that matrix multiplication is *not* commutative: there are matrices $\mathbf{A}$ and $\mathbf{B}$ for which the product $\mathbf{AB}$ exists but the product $\mathbf{BA}$ does not. Moreover, even when both products are defined, $\mathbf{AB}$ is usually not equal to $\mathbf{BA}$.

## 4.2   The inverse of a matrix

> For more detail on the topics covered in this subsection, refer to Section 3 of MST124 Unit 9.

If you multiply a number by 1, then the number is unchanged. An **identity matrix** is a matrix that behaves like the number 1, in the sense that if a matrix $\mathbf{A}$ is multiplied by an identity matrix of an appropriate size, then the result is again $\mathbf{A}$.

The definition of an identity matrix is summarised in the box below.

---

**Identity matrices**

An **identity matrix** is a square matrix $\mathbf{I}$ such that

- for any matrix $\mathbf{A}$ for which the product $\mathbf{AI}$ is defined, $\mathbf{AI} = \mathbf{A}$
- for any matrix $\mathbf{A}$ for which the product $\mathbf{IA}$ is defined, $\mathbf{IA} = \mathbf{A}$.

Each identity matrix has the form

$$\begin{pmatrix} 1 & 0 & 0 & \cdots & 0 \\ 0 & 1 & 0 & \cdots & 0 \\ 0 & 0 & 1 & \cdots & 0 \\ \vdots & \vdots & \vdots & \ddots & \vdots \\ 0 & 0 & 0 & \cdots & 1 \end{pmatrix}.$$

That is, it has ones down the leading diagonal and zeros elsewhere.

---

**Activity 29**   *Checking the properties of an identity matrix*

Let $\mathbf{A} = \begin{pmatrix} a_{11} & a_{12} \\ a_{21} & a_{22} \end{pmatrix}$     $\mathbf{B} = \begin{pmatrix} b_{11} & b_{12} \end{pmatrix}$     and     $\mathbf{I} = \begin{pmatrix} 1 & 0 \\ 0 & 1 \end{pmatrix}$.

(a) Show that $\mathbf{AI} = \mathbf{IA} = \mathbf{A}$.

(b) Show that $\mathbf{BI} = \mathbf{B}$ and explain why $\mathbf{IB}$ does not exist.

Now consider the two matrices

$$\mathbf{A} = \begin{pmatrix} 3 & 1 \\ 5 & 2 \end{pmatrix} \text{ and } \mathbf{B} = \begin{pmatrix} 2 & -1 \\ -5 & 3 \end{pmatrix}.$$

We can form the product $\mathbf{AB}$:

$$\mathbf{AB} = \begin{pmatrix} 3 & 1 \\ 5 & 2 \end{pmatrix} \begin{pmatrix} 2 & -1 \\ -5 & 3 \end{pmatrix} = \begin{pmatrix} 1 & 0 \\ 0 & 1 \end{pmatrix}.$$

Similarly, we can form the product $\mathbf{BA}$:

$$\mathbf{BA} = \begin{pmatrix} 2 & -1 \\ -5 & 3 \end{pmatrix} \begin{pmatrix} 3 & 1 \\ 5 & 2 \end{pmatrix} = \begin{pmatrix} 1 & 0 \\ 0 & 1 \end{pmatrix}.$$

Hence,

$$\mathbf{AB} = \mathbf{I} \text{ and } \mathbf{BA} = \mathbf{I}.$$

In general, if $\mathbf{A}$ and $\mathbf{B}$ are any two $n \times n$ matrices with the property that

$$\mathbf{AB} = \mathbf{I} \text{ and } \mathbf{BA} = \mathbf{I},$$

where $\mathbf{I}$ is the $n \times n$ identity matrix, then $\mathbf{B}$ is known as the **inverse** of $\mathbf{A}$.

When the inverse of a matrix $\mathbf{A}$ exists, it is unique.

We usually write the inverse of a matrix $\mathbf{A}$ as $\mathbf{A}^{-1}$.

Now let's look at how to find the inverse of a $2 \times 2$ matrix. The first step is to check that the inverse exists, and you can do that by working out the **determinant** of the matrix, as follows.

---

**Determinant of a $2 \times 2$ matrix**

Let $\mathbf{A} = \begin{pmatrix} a & b \\ c & d \end{pmatrix}$. Then the number $ad - bc$ is called the **determinant** of $\mathbf{A}$, written det $\mathbf{A}$.

If the determinant of $\mathbf{A}$ is not zero, then $\mathbf{A}$ has an inverse and we say that $\mathbf{A}$ is **invertible**.

If the determinant of $\mathbf{A}$ is zero, then $\mathbf{A}$ does not have an inverse and we say that $\mathbf{A}$ is **non-invertible**.

---

Sometimes, non-invertible matrices are called *singular* matrices, and invertible matrices are called *non-singular* matrices.

You may also see the notation $|\mathbf{A}|$, for the determinant of the matrix $\mathbf{A}$. This notation is also used when a matrix is written out in full, for example

$$\begin{vmatrix} 1 & -2 \\ 3 & -1 \end{vmatrix} = 1 \times (-1) - (-2) \times (3) = 5.$$

If the determinant of a $2 \times 2$ matrix is not zero, then you can use the following formula to find the inverse of the matrix. It is also possible to work out the inverses of larger square matrices, but the process is more complicated.

---

**Inverse of a $2 \times 2$ matrix**

The inverse of the $2 \times 2$ matrix $\begin{pmatrix} a & b \\ c & d \end{pmatrix}$ is given by

$$\frac{1}{ad - bc} \begin{pmatrix} d & -b \\ -c & a \end{pmatrix}, \quad \text{provided that } ad - bc \neq 0.$$

In other words, to obtain the inverse when $ad - bc \neq 0$, swap the two elements on the leading diagonal and multiply the other two elements by $-1$, then multiply the resulting matrix by the scalar $1/(ad - bc)$.

---

**Example 12** *Inverses of $2 \times 2$ matrices*

For each of the following matrices, check whether its inverse exists and, if it does, find it.

(a) $\begin{pmatrix} \sqrt{2} & \frac{1}{2} \\ 4 & \sqrt{2} \end{pmatrix}$    (b) $\begin{pmatrix} -2 & 4 \\ 1 & 3 \end{pmatrix}$

**Solution**

(a) Let $\mathbf{A} = \begin{pmatrix} \sqrt{2} & \frac{1}{2} \\ 4 & \sqrt{2} \end{pmatrix}$.

   🔍 Check the determinant of $\mathbf{A}$ to see whether an inverse exists. 💬

   $$\det \mathbf{A} = \sqrt{2} \times \sqrt{2} - 4 \times \tfrac{1}{2} = 2 - 2 = 0.$$

   Since $\det \mathbf{A} = 0$, the matrix does not have an inverse.

(b) Let $\mathbf{B} = \begin{pmatrix} -2 & 4 \\ 1 & 3 \end{pmatrix}$.

   🔍 Check the determinant of $\mathbf{B}$ to see whether an inverse exists. 💬

   $$\det \mathbf{B} = -2 \times 3 - 1 \times 4 = -6 - 4 = -10.$$

   Since $\det \mathbf{B} \neq 0$, the matrix has an inverse.

   🔍 Use the formula to write down the inverse of $\mathbf{B}$. 💬

   The inverse of $\mathbf{B}$ is

   $$\mathbf{B}^{-1} = -\tfrac{1}{10} \begin{pmatrix} 3 & -4 \\ -1 & -2 \end{pmatrix} = \tfrac{1}{10} \begin{pmatrix} -3 & 4 \\ 1 & 2 \end{pmatrix}.$$

---

You can practise inverting $2 \times 2$ matrices in the next activity.

**Activity 30** *Finding inverses of $2 \times 2$ matrices*

Determine which of the following matrices are invertible. For those that are, write down the inverse.

(a) $\mathbf{A} = \begin{pmatrix} 3 & 1 \\ -2 & 4 \end{pmatrix}$    (b) $\mathbf{B} = \begin{pmatrix} 3 & 9 \\ 2 & 6 \end{pmatrix}$    (c) $\mathbf{C} = \begin{pmatrix} -\frac{1}{2} & \frac{2}{3} \\ 6 & -3 \end{pmatrix}$

# 5 Differentiation

This section summarises some of the key ideas about differentiation that are explained more fully in MST124 Units 6 and 7.

Differentiation and integration (which is revised in Section 6) are two of the most important topics in higher mathematics. You will need to be fluent in using all the techniques in these two sections.

Try the following quiz to determine which topics you need to revise thoroughly.

**Activity 31** *Differentiation quiz*

(a) Differentiate each of the following functions

    (i)  $y = (2x - 1)\left(3x^2 - \dfrac{4}{x}\right)$

    (ii)  $y = e^{\cos(2x)}$

    (iii)  $h(x) = x^3(\cos(2x) + \sin(2x))$

    (iv)  $s(t) = \dfrac{t}{\ln t}$

(b) Consider the function
$$f(x) = 3x^4 + 4x^3 - 12x^2 + 1.$$

Find the coordinates of the stationary points and determine whether each is a local minimum, a local maximum or a point of inflection.

(c) A particle moves along a straight line. The displacement $s$ (in m) of the particle at time $t$ (in s) is given by
$$s = 50t - 5t^2.$$

Find an expression for the velocity $v$ at time $t$. Hence find the maximum displacement of the particle.

## 5.1 Finding derivatives of simple functions

For more detail on the topics covered in this subsection, refer to Sections 1 and 2 of MST124 Unit 6.

The gradient of a straight line measures how steep the line is. It can be calculated from the coordinates of any two points on the line, provided that the line is not vertical.

A very steep gradient!

**Gradient of a straight line**

The gradient of the straight line through the points $(x_1, y_1)$ and $(x_2, y_2)$, where $x_1 \neq x_2$, is given by

$$\text{gradient} = \frac{y_2 - y_1}{x_2 - x_1}.$$

For example, the gradient of the line through the points $(2, -2)$ and $(-1, 4)$ is given by

$$\text{gradient} = \frac{4 - (-2)}{-1 - 2} = \frac{6}{-3} = -2.$$

The gradient of a straight line can be positive, negative or zero. A straight line that slopes *down* from left to right has a *negative* gradient and a straight line that slopes *up* has a *positive* gradient. A horizontal line has a gradient of zero and a vertical line does not have a gradient.

The gradient of a curved graph at a particular point is the same as the gradient of the **tangent** to the graph at that point, as shown in Figure 27(a). The tangent can be visualised by imagining 'zooming in' on the point, as shown in Figure 27(b).

As you zoom in, the portion of the graph around the point looks straighter and straighter and eventually it will appear indistinguishable from a line segment through the point. This line segment is part of the tangent to the graph at that point.

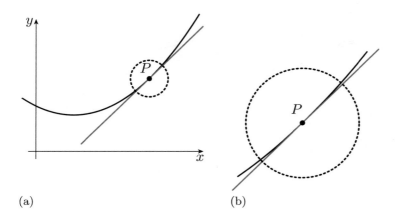

(a)                                          (b)

**Figure 27** (a) The tangent at the point $P$ (b) zooming in on $P$

The tangent to a curved graph at a point may just touch the curve at that point, as with the tangent at $P$ in Figure 28(a), or it may cross the curve at that point, as with the tangent at $Q$ in Figure 28(b).

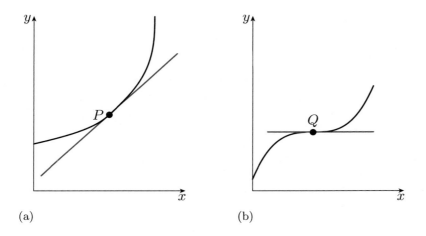

(a)                                          (b)

**Figure 28** (a) Tangent at $P$ touches the curve (b) tangent at $Q$ crosses the curve

For many of the functions that you will meet in MST125, the graph of the function has a tangent at every point. However, this is not always the case. For example, Figure 29 shows the graph of the modulus function $f(x) = |x|$. Zooming in on the point $(0, 0)$ will always give a V-shape rather than a line segment. Hence there is no tangent to the graph at this point.

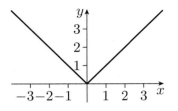

**Figure 29**   The graph of the modulus function $f(x) = |x|$

The idea of the gradient at a point on the graph of the function $f$ is used to define the derivative of the function, as in the box below.

### Derivatives

The **derivative** (or **derived function**) of a function $f$ is the function $f'$ such that

$f'(x) =$ gradient of the graph of $f$ at the point $(x, f(x))$.

The domain of $f'$ consists of the values in the domain of $f$ at which $f$ is **differentiable** (that is, the $x$-values that give points at which the gradient exists).

If $y = f(x)$, then $f'(x)$ is also denoted by $\dfrac{dy}{dx}$.

The derivative $f'$ is given by the equation

$$f'(x) = \lim_{h \to 0} \frac{f(x+h) - f(x)}{h}.$$

The procedure of using this equation to find a formula for the derivative $f'$ is called **differentiation from first principles**.

The notation $f'$ for the derivative of a function $f$ is known as **Lagrange notation**. The notation $\dfrac{dy}{dx}$, read as 'd y by d x' and often referred to as the **derivative of $y$ with respect to $x$**, is known as **Leibniz notation**. If $y = f(x)$, the notation $\dfrac{dy}{dx}$ means the same as $f'(x)$.

For example, if $f(x) = x^2$, then in Lagrange notation

$f'(x) = 2x,$

whilst in Leibniz notation,

if $y = x^2$,  then $\dfrac{dy}{dx} = 2x.$

You can also express the fact that $2x$ is the derivative of $x^2$ in Leibniz notation by writing $\dfrac{d}{dx}(x^2) = 2x$.

In practice, it is rarely necessary to use the process of differentiation from first principles. If you know the derivatives of some standard functions, you can use these to find the derivatives of other related functions.

The table below shows some standard functions and their derivatives. These results are explained fully in MST124, and you may find it helpful to review Section 2 of MST124 Unit 6 and Section 1 of MST124 Unit 7 before proceeding further with this subsection.

You should try to memorise at least the first six functions and their derivatives (those above the line in the middle of the table), as they're used frequently in mathematics. Note that the angles in the trigonometric functions in this table are measured in *radians*.

**Standard derivatives**

| Function $f(x)$ | Derivative $f'(x)$ |
| --- | --- |
| $a$ (constant) | $0$ |
| $x^n$ | $nx^{n-1}$ |
| $e^x$ | $e^x$ |
| $\ln x$ | $\dfrac{1}{x}$ |
| $\sin x$ | $\cos x$ |
| $\cos x$ | $-\sin x$ |
| $\tan x$ | $\sec^2 x$ |
| $\operatorname{cosec} x$ | $-\operatorname{cosec} x \cot x$ |
| $\sec x$ | $\sec x \tan x$ |
| $\cot x$ | $-\operatorname{cosec}^2 x$ |
| $\sin^{-1} x$ | $\dfrac{1}{\sqrt{1-x^2}}$ |
| $\cos^{-1} x$ | $-\dfrac{1}{\sqrt{1-x^2}}$ |
| $\tan^{-1} x$ | $\dfrac{1}{1+x^2}$ |

For example, using the fact that the derivative of $f(x) = x^n$ for any number $n$ is $f'(x) = nx^{n-1}$, you can work out that the derivative of

$$f(x) = \sqrt{x} = x^{\frac{1}{2}}$$

is

$$f'(x) = \frac{1}{2}x^{-\frac{1}{2}} = \frac{1}{2\sqrt{x}}.$$

If you multiply a function by a constant then, by differentiating from first principles, it can be shown that its derivative is multiplied by the same constant. This fact is known as the **constant multiple rule**. It is summarised in the boxes below using each of the two standard notations for derivatives.

**Constant multiple rule (Lagrange notation)**

If the function $k$ is given by $k(x) = af(x)$, where $f$ is a function and $a$ is a constant, then

$$k'(x) = af'(x),$$

for all values of $x$ at which $f$ is differentiable.

**Constant multiple rule (Leibniz notation)**

If $y = au$, where $u$ is a function of $x$ and $a$ is a constant, then

$$\frac{dy}{dx} = a\frac{du}{dx},$$

for all values of $x$ at which $u$ is differentiable.

For example, consider the expression

$$y = \frac{3}{x^2}.$$

This can be written as

$$y = 3 \times \frac{1}{x^2} = 3x^{-2},$$

and so

$$\frac{dy}{dx} = 3 \times (-2)x^{-3} = -6x^{-3} = -\frac{6}{x^3}.$$

It can also be shown that the derivative of the sum of two functions is the sum of the derivatives of the two functions. This general rule is stated in the boxes below.

**Sum rule (Lagrange notation)**

If $k(x) = f(x) + g(x)$, where $f$ and $g$ are functions, then

$$k'(x) = f'(x) + g'(x),$$

for all values of $x$ at which both $f$ and $g$ are differentiable.

**Sum rule (Leibniz notation)**

If $y = u + v$, where $u$ and $v$ are functions of $x$, then

$$\frac{dy}{dx} = \frac{du}{dx} + \frac{dv}{dx},$$

for all values of $x$ at which both $u$ and $v$ are differentiable.

For example, if $y = \cos x - \sin x$, then $\dfrac{dy}{dx} = -\sin x - \cos x.$

The next example illustrates how you can differentiate a wide range of functions by using the sum rule and the constant multiple rule in combination. Note that sometimes the function has to be rearranged first, in order to express its formula as a sum.

Throughout this section, the domains of functions you are asked to differentiate are not usually specified. You should assume that the domain is the largest possible subset of the real numbers on which the function can be defined, and that you are differentiating the function at a point where it is differentiable.

---

**Example 13**  *Using the sum rule and the constant multiple rule*

Differentiate each of the following functions.

(a)  $f(x) = \dfrac{3}{x} - 4\sqrt{x} + \frac{1}{4}e^x - 5\ln x$

(b)  $y = (3x - 1)(2x + 5)$

(c)  $s = \dfrac{3t + 4}{t^3}$

**Solution**

(a)  🔍 Express $f(x)$ in terms of functions from the table of standard derivatives. 💬

$$f(x) = \frac{3}{x} - 4\sqrt{x} + \tfrac{1}{4}e^x - 5\ln x$$
$$= 3x^{-1} - 4x^{\frac{1}{2}} + \tfrac{1}{4}e^x - 5\ln x.$$

🔍 Now use the sum rule and the constant multiple rule to find the derivative. 💬

Hence

$$f'(x) = 3 \times (-1)x^{-2} - 4 \times \tfrac{1}{2} \times x^{-\frac{1}{2}} + \tfrac{1}{4} \times e^x - 5 \times \frac{1}{x}$$
$$= -\frac{3}{x^2} - \frac{2}{\sqrt{x}} + \tfrac{1}{4}e^x - \frac{5}{x}.$$

(b)  🔍 Multiply out the brackets and then use the sum rule and the constant multiple rule. 💬

We have

$$y = (3x - 1)(2x + 5) = 6x^2 + 13x - 5,$$

so

$$\frac{dy}{dx} = 6 \times 2x + 13 - 0 = 12x + 13.$$

(c)  🔍 First expand the fraction to express it in terms of functions from the table of standard derivatives. 💬

$$s = \frac{3t+4}{t^3} = \frac{3t}{t^3} + \frac{4}{t^3} = 3t^{-2} + 4t^{-3}.$$

🔍 Now use the sum rule and the constant multiple rule. 💬

$$\frac{ds}{dt} = 3 \times (-2) \times t^{-3} + 4 \times (-3) \times t^{-4} = -\frac{6}{t^3} - \frac{12}{t^4}.$$

**Activity 32**   *Using the sum rule and the constant multiple rule*

Differentiate each of the following functions.

(a)  $f(x) = 2\sin x - 4\cos x + 5\tan x$

(b)  $g(x) = 7x^2 + \dfrac{5}{x} - x(2x^2 - 3) + 6$

(c)  $y = \ln(5x)$

(d)  $p = \dfrac{(q^2 - 3)(q + 1)}{q^2}$

## 5.2   The product, quotient and chain rules

For more detail on the topics covered in this subsection, refer to Section 2 of MST124 Unit 7.

If a function is a product of two or more polynomial functions, then you can multiply out the brackets and use the sum rule and the constant multiple rule to find the derivative of the function. However, for many functions which are products of other functions, it is not possible to rearrange the product in this way. In these cases, you can use the product rule, as explained in the boxes below.

**Product rule (Lagrange notation)**

If $k(x) = f(x)g(x)$, where $f$ and $g$ are functions, then

$$k'(x) = f(x)g'(x) + g(x)f'(x),$$

for all values of $x$ at which both $f$ and $g$ are differentiable.

**Product rule (Leibniz notation)**

If $y = uv$, where $u$ and $v$ are functions of $x$, then

$$\frac{dy}{dx} = u\frac{dv}{dx} + v\frac{du}{dx},$$

for all values of $x$ at which both $u$ and $v$ are differentiable.

---

**Example 14**   *Differentiating a product*

What is the gradient of the graph of $y = x^3 \cos x$ at the point on the graph where $x = \pi/2$? Give the exact answer.

**Solution**

To find the gradient of the graph, we need to work out the derivative of $y$ with respect to $x$. Differentiate $y$ using the product rule.

Let $u(x) = x^3$ and $v(x) = \cos x$.

Then $\dfrac{du}{dx} = 3x^2$ and $\dfrac{dv}{dx} = -\sin x$.

By the product rule,

$$\frac{dy}{dx} = u\frac{dv}{dx} + v\frac{du}{dx}$$
$$= x^3(-\sin x) + (\cos x)(3x^2)$$
$$= x^2(3\cos x - x\sin x).$$

Now substitute the value $x = \pi/2$ to find the gradient at this point.

The formula for $dy/dx$ then gives that the gradient at $x = \pi/2$ is

$$\left(\frac{\pi}{2}\right)^2 \left(3\cos\left(\frac{\pi}{2}\right) - \frac{\pi}{2}\sin\left(\frac{\pi}{2}\right)\right).$$

Since $\sin(\pi/2) = 1$ and $\cos(\pi/2) = 0$, the gradient is

$$-\left(\frac{\pi}{2}\right)^3 = -\frac{\pi^3}{8}.$$

---

You may prefer to remember the product rule in the following informal way:

$$\begin{pmatrix} \text{derivative} \\ \text{of product} \end{pmatrix} = (\text{first}) \times \begin{pmatrix} \text{derivative} \\ \text{of second} \end{pmatrix} + (\text{second}) \times \begin{pmatrix} \text{derivative} \\ \text{of first} \end{pmatrix}.$$

**Activity 33**   *Using the product rule*

(a)  Use the product rule to differentiate the following functions.

(i)  $k(x) = x \sin x$      (ii)  $y = e^x \tan x$      (iii)  $r = t^3 \ln t$

(b)  What is the gradient of the graph of the function $p(t) = \sqrt{t} \sec t$ at $t = \pi/3$? Give your answer to one decimal place.

Suppose now that two differentiable functions $f$ and $g$ can be combined to form a function $k$ whose rule is $k(x) = f(x)/g(x)$. Then the derivative of $k$ can be found by using the quotient rule, which is described in the boxes below.

**Quotient rule (Lagrange notation)**

If $k(x) = f(x)/g(x)$, where $f$ and $g$ are functions, then

$$k'(x) = \frac{g(x)f'(x) - f(x)g'(x)}{(g(x))^2},$$

for all values of $x$ at which both $f$ and $g$ are differentiable and $g(x) \neq 0$.

**Quotient rule (Leibniz notation)**

If $y = u/v$, where $u$ and $v$ are functions of $x$, then

$$\frac{dy}{dx} = \frac{v\dfrac{du}{dx} - u\dfrac{dv}{dx}}{v^2},$$

for all values of $x$ at which $u$ and $v$ are differentiable and $v \neq 0$.

**Example 15**   *Differentiating a quotient*

Differentiate the function

$$k(x) = \frac{x^2 + 1}{2x + 5}.$$

**Solution**

🔍 Identify two functions $f$ and $g$ such that $k(x) = f(x)/g(x)$. 💬

Here we put $f(x) = x^2 + 1$ and $g(x) = 2x + 5$.

🔍 Find their derivatives. 💬

Then $f'(x) = 2x$ and $g'(x) = 2$.

🔍 Now use the quotient rule. 💬

By the quotient rule,

$$k'(x) = \frac{g(x)f'(x) - f(x)g'(x)}{(g(x))^2}$$

$$= \frac{(2x+5)(2x) - (x^2+1) \times 2}{(2x+5)^2}$$

🔍 Finally, simplify the answer. 💬

$$= \frac{4x^2 + 10x - 2x^2 - 2}{(2x+5)^2} = \frac{2(x^2 + 5x - 1)}{(2x+5)^2}.$$

You may prefer to remember the quotient rule as in the following informal way, and apply it directly:

$$\begin{pmatrix} \text{derivative} \\ \text{of quotient} \end{pmatrix} = \frac{\text{bottom} \times \begin{pmatrix} \text{derivative} \\ \text{of top} \end{pmatrix} - (\text{top}) \times \begin{pmatrix} \text{derivative} \\ \text{of bottom} \end{pmatrix}}{(\text{bottom})^2}.$$

**Activity 34**  *Using the quotient rule*

Use the quotient rule to differentiate the following functions.

(a)  $k(x) = \dfrac{2x^3 + 1}{\ln x}$  (b)  $r(y) = \dfrac{e^y - 1}{e^y + 1}$  (c)  $y = \dfrac{x^3}{x^2 + x + 1}$

(d)  $m(n) = \tan n$

Now consider the function $y = \sin(2x)$. Since $\sin(2x) = 2\sin x \cos x$, you could use the product rule to differentiate this function.

However, an alternative method is to recognise $y$ as a composite of two functions. To work out $y$ for a particular value of $x$, you first have to multiply $x$ by 2. Let's call the result $u$, so $u = 2x$. Then you find the sine of the result, so $y = \sin u$. This shows that $y$ can be decomposed into the two functions,

$$y = \sin u, \text{ where } u = 2x.$$

Alternatively, you can think of $y = \sin(2x)$ as $y = \sin(\text{'something'})$. Now letting $u = \text{'something'}$ also gives $u = 2x$ and $y = \sin u$.

Once you have recognised that a function is a composite of two other functions, you can use the chain rule to differentiate it. The chain rule is summarised in the boxes below. It is also sometimes called the *composite rule* or the *function of a function rule*.

**Chain rule (Lagrange notation)**

If the function $k$ has the rule $k(x) = g(f(x))$, where $f$ and $g$ are functions, then

$$k'(x) = g'(f(x))f'(x)$$

for all values of $x$ such that $f$ is differentiable at $x$ and $g$ is differentiable at $f(x)$.

**Chain rule (Leibniz notation)**

If $y$ is a function of $u$, where $u$ is a function of $x$, then

$$\frac{dy}{dx} = \frac{dy}{du}\frac{du}{dx}$$

for all values of $x$ where $y$ as a function of $u$, and $u$ as a function of $x$, are differentiable.

For example, to differentiate $y = \sin(2x)$, let $u = 2x$ and $y = \sin u$.

Then $\dfrac{du}{dx} = 2$ and $\dfrac{dy}{du} = \cos u$.

Hence, by the chain rule,

$$\begin{aligned}
\frac{dy}{dx} &= \frac{dy}{du}\frac{du}{dx} \\
&= (\cos u) \times 2 \\
&= 2\cos(2x).
\end{aligned}$$

When you are confident with using the chain rule, you may prefer to apply it in the following informal way, without introducing the extra variable $u$.

Suppose $y$ is a function of 'something', where the 'something' is a function of $x$. Then, to differentiate $y$ with respect to $x$, you first differentiate $y$ with respect to the 'something' and then multiply by the derivative of the 'something' with respect to $x$.

For example, suppose

$$y = \sin^3 x = (\sin x)^3.$$

Then $y =$ 'something' cubed, where the 'something' is $\sin x$.

Now the derivative of 'something' cubed with respect to 'something' is

$$3 \times \text{'something' squared,}$$

and the derivative of the 'something' with respect to $x$ is $\cos x$.

So, if $y = \sin^3 x$, then $\dfrac{dy}{dx} = 3 \sin^2 x \cos x$.

---

**Example 16**   *Differentiating composite functions using the chain rule*

Find the derivative of each of the following functions.

(a)  $y = (x^2 - 3x + 2)^{12}$      (b)  $w = \cos(\sqrt{t})$

(c)  $r(s) = \dfrac{3}{\sqrt{s^2 + 2s + 5}}$

**Solution**

(a)  🔍 Here, $y$ has the form $y = (\text{something})^{12}$, so set something $= u$. 💬

If we put $u = x^2 - 3x + 2$, then $y = u^{12}$.

🔍 Next, find the derivatives of $u$ and $y$. 💬

We have
$$\frac{du}{dx} = 2x - 3 \quad \text{and} \quad \frac{dy}{du} = 12u^{11}.$$

🔍 Now apply the chain rule. 💬

By the chain rule,
$$\begin{aligned}
\frac{dy}{dx} &= \frac{dy}{du}\frac{du}{dx} \\
&= 12u^{11} \times (2x - 3) \\
&= 12(x^2 - 3x + 2)^{11}(2x - 3).
\end{aligned}$$

(b) Here $w = \cos(\sqrt{t})$. If we let $u = \sqrt{t} = t^{\frac{1}{2}}$, then $w = \cos u$. So
$$\frac{du}{dt} = \frac{1}{2}t^{-\frac{1}{2}} \quad \text{and} \quad \frac{dw}{du} = -\sin u.$$

Hence, by the chain rule
$$\begin{aligned}
\frac{dw}{dt} &= \frac{dw}{du}\frac{du}{dt} \\
&= (-\sin u)\left(\frac{1}{2}t^{-\frac{1}{2}}\right) \\
&= \left(-\sin\sqrt{t}\right)\left(\frac{1}{2}t^{-\frac{1}{2}}\right) \\
&= -\frac{\sin\sqrt{t}}{2\sqrt{t}}.
\end{aligned}$$

(c)  We have $r(s) = \dfrac{3}{\sqrt{s^2 + 2s + 5}}$.

> 💭 This function is 3 over the square root of 'something'. Rewrite the function as a power of the something. 💭

So

$$r(s) = 3(s^2 + 2s + 5)^{-\frac{1}{2}}.$$

> 💭 Think of $s^2 + 2s + 5$ as the something, so $r = 3 \times (\text{something})^{-\frac{1}{2}}$. Now differentiate directly. 💭

By the chain rule,

$$r'(s) = 3 \times \left(-\tfrac{1}{2}\right)(s^2 + 2s + 5)^{-\frac{3}{2}} \times (2s + 2)$$
$$= -\frac{3(s + 1)}{(s^2 + 2s + 5)^{\frac{3}{2}}}.$$

---

**Activity 35**  *Differentiating composite functions using the chain rule*

Find the derivative of each of the following functions.

(a)  $y = e^{x^2}$ (this function may also be written as $y = \exp(x^2)$)

(b)  $r = \sqrt{s^4 + 2s^2 + 3}$

(c)  $g(x) = \tan(cx)$, where $c$ is a constant

(d)  $s(p) = \ln(p^4 + 1)$

It can sometimes be difficult to decide which differentiation rules to apply, particularly if the function involves a combination of products, quotients or composites. You'll see an example of how to deal with functions like this shortly, but first here is a checklist of useful questions to help you to decide which method to use.

**Checklist for differentiating a function**

- Is it a standard function?
- Can you use the constant multiple rule and/or the sum rule?
- Can you rewrite it to make it easier to differentiate? For example, multiplying out brackets may help.
- Can you use the product rule (is it of the form $f(x) = \text{something} \times \text{something}$)?
- Can you use the quotient rule (is it of the form $f(x) = \text{something}/\text{something}$)?
- Can you use the chain rule (is it of the form $f(x) = \text{a function of something}$)?

When you use a differentiation rule, you usually have to find the derivatives of simpler functions. You can apply the checklist above to each of these simpler functions in turn.

The next example illustrates how the differentiation rules can be combined. Note that, for complicated functions, it can be helpful to work in steps, using the notation $\mathrm{d}/\mathrm{d}x$ to indicate the derivative of a function that appears in the working.

---

**Example 17**   *Combining the differentiation rules*

Find the derivative of $y = 2xe^{\cos x}$.

**Solution**

🔍 This is a product of two functions, $2x$ and $e^{\cos x}$, so apply the product rule. 💬

By the product rule,

$$\frac{\mathrm{d}y}{\mathrm{d}x} = 2x\frac{\mathrm{d}}{\mathrm{d}x}(e^{\cos x}) + e^{\cos x}\frac{\mathrm{d}}{\mathrm{d}x}(2x)$$

$$= 2x\frac{\mathrm{d}}{\mathrm{d}x}(e^{\cos x}) + 2e^{\cos x}.$$

🔍 Now work out the derivative of $e^{\cos x}$. The function $e^{\cos x}$ is of the form $e^{\text{something}}$, so use the chain rule. 💬

$$\frac{\mathrm{d}}{\mathrm{d}x}(e^{\cos x}) = (e^{\cos x})(-\sin x).$$

🔍 Finally, combine the results and simplify the answer. 💬

$$\frac{\mathrm{d}y}{\mathrm{d}x} = 2x(e^{\cos x})(-\sin x) + 2e^{\cos x}$$

$$= (2e^{\cos x})(1 - x\sin x).$$

---

**Activity 36**    *Combining the differentiation rules*

Differentiate the following functions.

(a)  $z = \cos(2\theta)\sin(4\theta)$       (b)  $f(x) = \dfrac{x\cos x}{x^2 + 4}$

## 5.3  Stationary points

> For more detail on the topics covered in this subsection, refer to
> Section 4 of MST124 Unit 6.

The derivative of a function tells you the gradient at each point on the
graph of the function. A positive gradient corresponds to a graph sloping
up, while a negative gradient corresponds to a graph sloping down. So the
derivative of a function tells you whether the function is increasing or
decreasing, as set out in the box below. (If you need to refresh your
memory about increasing or decreasing functions, look again at the box in
Subsection 1.4 of this unit.)

Thank goodness for the stationary points!

**Increasing/decreasing criterion**

If $f'(x)$ is positive for all $x$ in an interval $I$, then $f$ is increasing on $I$.

If $f'(x)$ is negative for all $x$ in an interval $I$, then $f$ is decreasing on $I$.

A point at which the gradient of a graph is zero is called a **stationary
point**. The stationary points of a function $f$ can be found by solving the
equation $f'(x) = 0$.

Both the $x$-coordinate and the point itself are known as the stationary
point. For example, you can say: 'The function has a stationary point at
$x = 2$' or 'The stationary point has coordinates $(2, 6)$'.

Figure 30 shows some examples of stationary points, namely a local
maximum (a), a local minimum (b) and a horizontal point of inflection (c).
A horizontal point of inflection occurs when the function is decreasing (or
increasing) on *both* sides of the stationary point.

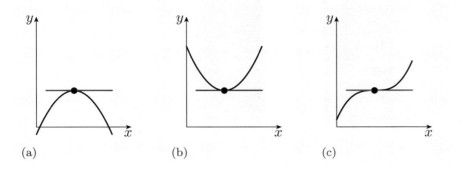

**Figure 30**   (a) A local maximum (b) a local minimum (c) a horizontal point of inflection

Note that not all stationary points are one of these types. For example, the line $y = 5$ has zero gradient everywhere and hence all points on the line are stationary points.

You can determine the nature of a stationary point by considering the sign of the derivative on either side of the stationary point, as outlined in the box below.

**First derivative test (for determining the nature of a stationary point of a function $f$)**

If there are open intervals immediately to the left and right of a stationary point such that

- $f'(x)$ is positive on the left interval and negative on the right interval, then the stationary point is a local maximum

- $f'(x)$ is negative on the left interval and positive on the right interval, then the stationary point is a local minimum

- $f'(x)$ is positive on both intervals or negative on both intervals, then the stationary point is a horizontal point of inflection.

This test is called the *first derivative test* because it is based on looking at the values of $f'(x)$, that is, the function $f$ differentiated *once*. The test is illustrated in Figure 31. The signs show whether the derivative is positive or negative on intervals immediately to the left and right of the stationary point.

Suppose that a function is differentiable at all points within an interval around the stationary point, and that there are no other stationary points within this interval. Then it is possible to apply the first derivative test by choosing two points within the interval, on either side of the stationary point, and working out the value of the derivative at these points.

This process is illustrated in the next example. Note that the function in this example is a polynomial and so is differentiable everywhere.

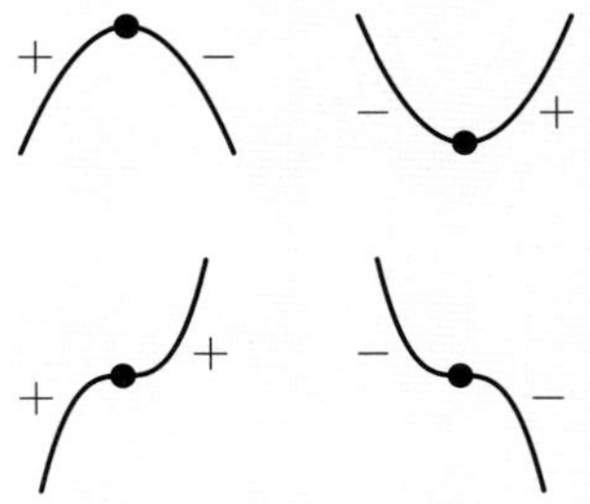

**Figure 31**   The signs of the derivative to the left and right of different types of stationary point

**Example 18**    *Determining the nature of stationary points by applying the first derivative test*

Consider the function
$$f(x) = 2x^3 - \tfrac{9}{2}x^2 - 6x + 6.$$

(a)  Find the coordinates of the stationary points of $f$.

(b)  Determine whether each stationary point of $f$ is a local maximum, a local minimum or a horizontal point of inflection.

(c)  Hence sketch the graph of $f$.

(d)  What are the greatest and the least values of the function on the interval $[-1, 4]$?

**Solution**

(a)  🔍 Differentiate $f$ and solve the equation $f'(x) = 0$. 💬

The derivative is
$$\begin{aligned}
f'(x) &= 6x^2 - 9x - 6 \\
&= 3(2x^2 - 3x - 2) \\
&= 3(2x + 1)(x - 2).
\end{aligned}$$

Thus the equation $f'(x) = 0$ gives
$$3(2x + 1)(x - 2) = 0,$$
which has solutions
$$x = -\tfrac{1}{2} \text{ and } x = 2.$$

Hence the stationary points of $f$ are $-\tfrac{1}{2}$ and $2$. Now
$$f\left(-\tfrac{1}{2}\right) = 2\left(-\tfrac{1}{2}\right)^3 - \tfrac{9}{2}\left(-\tfrac{1}{2}\right)^2 - 6\left(-\tfrac{1}{2}\right) + 6 = \tfrac{61}{8},$$
and
$$f(2) = 2 \times 2^3 - \tfrac{9}{2} \times 2^2 - 6 \times 2 + 6 = -8.$$

The coordinates of the stationary points are therefore $\left(-\tfrac{1}{2}, \tfrac{61}{8}\right)$ and $(2, -8)$.

(b)  🔍 Choose points on either side of each stationary point at which to apply the first derivative test. There are many possible choices of such points, so choose them to be as simple as possible. 💬

Consider the values $-1$, $0$ and $3$. The values $-1$ and $0$ lie on each side of the stationary point $-\tfrac{1}{2}$, and the values $0$ and $3$ lie on each side of the stationary point $2$.

As the function $f$ is a polynomial function, it is differentiable at all values of $x$. Also, there are no stationary points between $-1$ and $-\frac{1}{2}$, or between $-\frac{1}{2}$ and $0$. Similarly, there are no stationary points between $0$ and $2$, or between $2$ and $3$. Since $f'(x) = 6x^2 - 9x - 6$, we have

$$f'(-1) = 6(-1)^2 - 9(-1) - 6 = 9$$
$$f'(0) = -6$$
$$f'(3) = 6(3)^2 - 9(3) - 6 = 21.$$

Hence $f'$ is positive at $-1$ and negative at $0$, so the stationary point at $x = -\frac{1}{2}$ is a local maximum, whilst $f'$ is negative at $0$ and positive at $3$, so the stationary point at $x = 2$ is a local minimum.

(c)  🔍 Sketch the graph of $f$ and label the coordinates of the key points. 💬

The graph of $f$ is shown below, with the part of the graph lying in the interval $[-1, 4]$ highlighted (this is useful for part (d)).

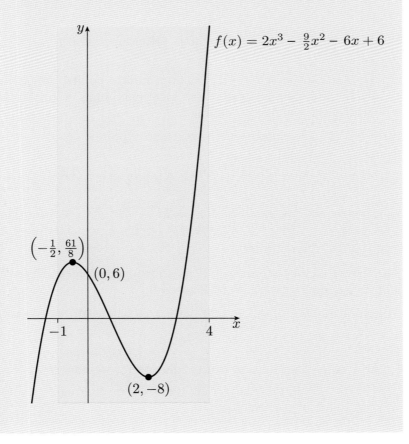

(d) 🔍 Find the values of $f$ at the endpoints of the interval $[-1, 4]$ and compare with the $y$-coordinates of the stationary points. 💬

$$f(-1) = 2 \times (-1)^3 - \tfrac{9}{2} \times (-1)^2 - 6 \times (-1) + 6 = \tfrac{11}{2}.$$

$$f(4) = 2 \times 4^3 - \tfrac{9}{2} \times 4^2 - 6 \times 4 + 6 = 38.$$

The $y$-coordinates of the local minimum and the local maximum are $-8$ and $\tfrac{61}{8}$ respectively. Hence the least value and the greatest value of the function $f$ on the interval $[-1, 4]$ are $-8$ and $38$ respectively.

---

**Activity 37**   *Determining the nature of stationary points using the first derivative test*

Consider the function

$$f(x) = x^4 - \tfrac{8}{3}x^3 + 2x^2 - 1.$$

(a) Find the stationary points of $f$. (Hint: factorise $f'(x)$, by first noticing that it has $x$ as a factor.)

(b) By finding the values of $f'$ at appropriate points, determine whether each stationary point of $f$ is a local maximum, a local minimum or a horizontal point of inflection.

(c) Find the coordinates of the stationary points.

(d) Hence sketch the graph of $f$.

Consider again the function $f(x) = 2x^3 - \tfrac{9}{2}x^2 - 6x + 6$ from Example 18. The derivative of $f(x)$ is $f'(x) = 6x^2 - 9x - 6$, which is itself a function that can be differentiated.

The derivative of the function $f'$ is known as the **second derivative** of $f$ and, in Lagrange notation, is denoted by $f''$.

In Leibniz notation, the second derivative of $y$ with respect to $x$ is denoted by $\dfrac{\mathrm{d}^2 y}{\mathrm{d}x^2}$ (read as 'd two $y$ by d $x$ squared').

In the case of the function from Example 18, we have $f''(x) = 12x - 9$ using Lagrange notation or, if we put $y = 2x^3 - \tfrac{9}{2}x^2 - 6x + 6$,

$$\frac{\mathrm{d}^2 y}{\mathrm{d}x^2} = 12x - 9,$$

using Leibniz notation.

Higher derivatives (that is, third derivatives, fourth derivatives, and so on) can be denoted in a similar way.

Now consider what we can say about the graph of a function $f$ from the values of its second derivative $f''$.

If the second derivative $f''$ is positive on an interval, then the derivative $f'$ must be increasing on the interval, and so the gradient of the graph of $f$ will be increasing. If the gradient of a graph is increasing on an interval, then the tangents at points within the interval lie below the curve and the graph is said to be **concave up**. Some examples of sections of graphs with increasing gradients are shown in Figure 32.

**Figure 32**   Sections of graphs with increasing gradients

On the other hand, if the second derivative $f''$ is negative on an interval, then the derivative $f'$ must be decreasing on the interval, and so the gradient of the graph of $f$ will be decreasing. In this case, the tangents at points on the graph within the interval lie above the curve and the graph is said to be **concave down**. Some sections of graphs with decreasing gradients are shown in Figure 33.

**Figure 33**   Sections of graphs with decreasing gradients

At and around a local maximum of a function, the gradient of its graph decreases and the second derivative is negative. At and around a local minimum of a function, the gradient of its graph increases and the second derivative is positive.

This gives a useful test for determining the nature of stationary points, which is summarised in the box below.

> **Second derivative test (for determining the nature of a stationary point)**
>
> If, at a stationary point of a function, the value of the second derivative of the function is
>
> - negative, then the stationary point is a local maximum
> - positive, then the stationary point is a local minimum.

From Example 18, you know that the stationary points of the function $f(x) = 2x^3 - \frac{9}{2}x^2 - 6x + 6$ occur at $x = -\frac{1}{2}$ and at $x = 2$. Substituting these values in the second derivative, $f''(x) = 12x - 9$, gives

$$f''(-\tfrac{1}{2}) = 12 \times \left(-\tfrac{1}{2}\right) - 9 = -15$$

and

$$f''(2) = 12 \times 2 - 9 = 15.$$

Since $f''(-\frac{1}{2})$ is negative, there is a local maximum at $x = -\frac{1}{2}$, and since $f''(2)$ is positive, there is a local minimum at $x = 2$. These results agree with those obtained from the first derivative test in Example 18.

Notice that, if the value of the second derivative of a function is *zero* at a stationary point, then the second derivative test can't be used to determine the nature of the stationary point. In this case, you should fall back on the first derivative test, which can always be used.

For example, consider the function $f(x) = x^4$. Then $f'(x) = 4x^3$ and hence there is a stationary point at $x = 0$. Differentiating $f'(x)$ gives $f''(x) = 12x^2$, and hence $f''(0) = 0$. So the second derivative is zero rather than either negative or positive, and therefore the second derivative test cannot be used to determine the nature of the stationary point.

However, the first derivative test can be used. When $x < 0$, $f'(x) < 0$, and when $x > 0$, $f'(x) > 0$, so the stationary point at $x = 0$ is a minimum.

The next activity asks you to apply the second derivative test to determine the nature of some stationary points.

**Activity 38**  *Determining the nature of stationary points using the second derivative test*

Consider the function

$$f(x) = 3x^4 + \tfrac{1}{3}x^3 - \tfrac{1}{2}x^2 + 5.$$

(a)  Find the stationary points of $f$.

(b)  Use the second derivative test to determine the nature of each stationary point.

A point where the graph of a function changes from concave up to concave down is called a **point of inflection**. The tangent to the graph at a point of inflection crosses the graph.

For example the graph of $y = x - x^3$ shown in Figure 34 has a point of inflection at the origin.

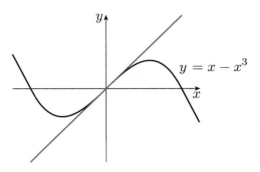

**Figure 34**    The graph of $y = x - x^3$; the tangent at $x = 0$ crosses the graph

The points of inflection of a function $f$ can be found by solving the equation $f''(x) = 0$ and checking that $f''(x)$ *changes sign* at these points.

Notice that a point of inflection is not necessarily a stationary point. However, if the gradient of the graph is zero at the point of inflection (that is, if $f'(x) = 0$), then the point is a *horizontal* point of inflection, which is a type of stationary point covered earlier.

---

**Activity 39**    *Finding points of inflection*

For each of the following functions, determine whether the graph of the function has any points of inflection.

(a)  $f(x) = x^3 - 3x^2 - 10x + 20$     (b)  $g(x) = x^4 - 8x^3 + 24x^2 - 32x + 40$

---

## 5.4    Rates of change

> For more detail on the topics covered in this subsection, refer to Sections 3 and 5 of MST124 Unit 6.

The gradient at any point on the graph of the variable $y$ against the variable $x$ measures the rate of change of $y$ with respect to $x$.

For example, suppose the displacement of an object moving along a straight line is plotted against time. Then the gradient of the resulting graph is the rate of change of the object's displacement with respect to time, that is, its **velocity**.

Similarly, if the velocity of the object is plotted against time, then the gradient of the resulting graph is the rate of change of the object's velocity with respect to time, that is, its **acceleration**.

(Acceleration, velocity and displacement are all vector quantities but, for motion along a straight line, they can be represented by scalars with the sign of the scalar indicating the direction.)

So, given a formula for the displacement of an object moving along a straight line in terms of time, you can find formulas for the velocity and acceleration of the object by differentiating the displacement function, as summarised in the box below.

> ### Displacement, velocity and acceleration
>
> Suppose that an object is moving along a straight line. If $t$ is the time that has elapsed since some chosen point in time, and $s$, $v$ and $a$ are the displacement, velocity and acceleration of the object, respectively, then
> $$v = \frac{ds}{dt}, \quad a = \frac{dv}{dt} \quad \text{and} \quad a = \frac{d^2s}{dt^2}.$$

Time, displacement, velocity and acceleration can be measured in any suitable units, as long as they are consistent. For example, if displacement is measured in metres (m) and time is measured in seconds (s), then velocity will be measured in 'metres per second' ($\text{m s}^{-1}$ or m/s) and acceleration in 'metres per second per second' ($\text{m s}^{-2}$ or m/s$^2$).

The next activity will give you some practice in working with these ideas.

**Activity 40**  *Using differentiation to investigate motion along a straight line*

A ball is thrown vertically upwards. The height of the ball above ground level is represented by the equation

$$s = 1.1 + 7t - 5t^2,$$

where $t$ is the time in seconds and $s$ is the height in metres.

(a) Find formulas for the ball's velocity and acceleration in terms of time.

(b) Find the ball's velocity and acceleration 0.4 seconds after it is thrown.

(c) When the ball reaches its maximum height, its velocity is zero. At what time does the ball reach its maximum height?

(d) Find the maximum height reached by the ball.

# 6 Integration

This section reviews some of the material on integration that you met in MST124 Unit 7 and Unit 8. Other aspects of integration will be reviewed when you study Unit 7, *Topics in calculus*.

Integration is the reverse of differentiation, which you reviewed in the previous section. The ideas and methods of integration underpin many topics in mathematics, so take time to work through the examples and activities in this section carefully.

Try the following quiz to determine which topics in this section you need to revise thoroughly.

## Activity 41   *Integration quiz*

(a) Find the indefinite integrals of the following functions.

   (i) $f(x) = (x - 1)(2x + 1)$      (ii) $g(t) = \dfrac{t^2 - 4}{t^3}$

(b) Show that the derivative of $y = \sec(2x)$ is

$$\frac{dy}{dx} = 2\sec(2x)\tan(2x).$$

   Hence find the indefinite integral

$$\int \sec(2x)\tan(2x)\,dx.$$

(c) Evaluate the following definite integrals. Give exact answers.

   (i) $\displaystyle\int_1^2 \frac{(2x - 1)^2}{x^3}\,dx$

   (ii) $\displaystyle\int_0^{\pi/4} (\cos 3\theta - \sin \theta)\,d\theta$

(d) Find the area between the graph of $y = e^{4x}$ and the $x$-axis from $x = -1$ to $x = 1$. Give your answer to three significant figures.

(e) Explain why the following statement is incorrect.

$$\int_{-1}^1 \frac{1}{x^2}\,dx = \int_{-1}^1 x^{-2}\,dx = \left[-x^{-1}\right]_{-1}^1 = -1 - (1) = -2$$

## 6.1  Indefinite integration

> For more detail on the topics covered in this subsection, refer to
> Sections 4 and 6 of MST124 Unit 7.

Suppose you have a function $f$, and you want to find another function,
say $F$, whose derivative is $f$. The function $F$ is called an **antiderivative**
of the original function $f$. For example, an antiderivative of the function
$f(x) = 3x^2$ is the function $F(x) = x^3$, because the derivative of $x^3$ is $3x^2$.

The process of finding an antiderivative of a function is called **integration**.

Note that any function of the form $F(x) = x^3 + c$, where $c$ is a constant,
also has derivative $3x^2$. This general function $F(x) = x^3 + c$ is known as
the **indefinite integral** of $f$.

Since the constant $c$ can take any value, it is known as an **arbitrary
constant**, or the **constant of integration**. You can use any letter for
this constant.

When working on integration, you will normally deal with functions that
are continuous. Informally, a **continuous function** is one whose graph
has no discontinuities (that is, 'breaks'), or whose graph you can draw
without taking your pen off the paper. Every continuous function has an
antiderivative. To obtain the indefinite integral of a continuous function,
you add an arbitrary constant to any particular antiderivative of the
function.

The definitions of an antiderivative and the indefinite integral of a function
are summarised below.

> **Antiderivatives and indefinite integrals**
>
> Suppose that $f$ is a function.
>
> An **antiderivative** of $f$ is any specific function whose derivative is $f$.
>
> If $f$ is continuous, then the **indefinite integral** of $f$ is the *general*
> function obtained by adding an arbitrary constant $c$ to the formula
> for an antiderivative of $f$. It describes the complete family of
> antiderivatives of $f$.

We tend to denote the function we start with by a lower-case letter, for
example $f$, and use the corresponding upper-case letter, for example $F$, to
denote any of its antiderivatives or its indefinite integral.

However, a more common notation for the indefinite integral of $f(x)$ is to
use the **integral sign** $\int$, and to write

$$\int f(x)\,\mathrm{d}x.$$

For example, for any value of $n \neq -1$, the indefinite integral of $f(x) = x^n$ is

$$\int x^n \, dx = \frac{1}{n+1} x^{n+1} + c.$$

The function $f(x)$ that is to be integrated is known as the **integrand**.

Indefinite integrals of some standard functions are shown in the table below. You should try to memorise at least the first six functions and their indefinite integrals (those above the line in the middle of the table), as they're used frequently in mathematics.

**Standard indefinite integrals**

| Function | Indefinite integral |
| --- | --- |
| $a$ (constant) | $ax + c$ |
| $x^n$ $(n \neq -1)$ | $\frac{1}{n+1} x^{n+1} + c$ |
| $e^x$ | $e^x + c$ |
| $\frac{1}{x}$ | $\ln |x| + c$ <br> or $\ln x + c$, for $x > 0$ |
| $\sin x$ | $-\cos x + c$ |
| $\cos x$ | $\sin x + c$ |
| $\sec^2 x$ | $\tan x + c$ |
| $\operatorname{cosec}^2 x$ | $-\cot x + c$ |
| $\sec x \tan x$ | $\sec x + c$ |
| $\operatorname{cosec} x \cot x$ | $-\operatorname{cosec} x + c$ |
| $\frac{1}{\sqrt{1-x^2}}$ | $\sin^{-1} x + c$ <br> or $-\cos^{-1} x + c$ |
| $\frac{1}{1+x^2}$ | $\tan^{-1} x + c$ |

Once you know the indefinite integrals of some standard functions, you can obtain formulas for the indefinite integrals of sums and constant multiples of the functions by using the two rules below.

**Constant multiple rule and sum rule for indefinite integrals**

$$\int k f(x) \, dx = k \int f(x) \, dx, \quad \text{where } k \text{ is a constant}$$

$$\int (f(x) + g(x)) \, dx = \int f(x) \, dx + \int g(x) \, dx$$

Sometimes it is necessary to rearrange the integrand (for example, by multiplying out brackets) so that these rules can be applied. The next example illustrates this.

---

**Example 19**  *Using the constant multiple rule and the sum rule for indefinite integrals*

Find the indefinite integral

$$\int \frac{(2x-1)(3x+4)}{x^2}\,\mathrm{d}x.$$

**Solution**

🔍 Manipulate the integrand to get it into a form that allows you to use the constant multiple rule and the sum rule for indefinite integrals, together with standard indefinite integrals. 💬

$$\int \frac{(2x-1)(3x+4)}{x^2}\,\mathrm{d}x = \int \frac{6x^2+5x-4}{x^2}\,\mathrm{d}x$$

$$= \int \left(6 + \frac{5}{x} - \frac{4}{x^2}\right)\mathrm{d}x$$

$$= \int 6\,\mathrm{d}x + 5\int \frac{1}{x}\,\mathrm{d}x - 4\int x^{-2}\,\mathrm{d}x$$

$$= 6x + 5\ln|x| - 4 \times \frac{x^{-1}}{-1} + c,$$

$$= 6x + 5\ln|x| + \frac{4}{x} + c,$$

where $c$ is an arbitrary constant.

---

You can practise using these rules for indefinite integrals in the next activity.

---

**Activity 42**  *Using the constant multiple rule and the sum rule for indefinite integrals*

Find each of the following indefinite integrals by first expanding the integrand.

(a) $\displaystyle\int 3x(x-1)^2\,\mathrm{d}x$     (b) $\displaystyle\int (\operatorname{cosec} x)(\operatorname{cosec} x + \cot x)\,\mathrm{d}x$

---

Now consider the function $f(x) = \cos(ax)$, where $a$ is a constant. To integrate this function, you need to find a function whose derivative is $\cos(ax)$. You know that the derivative of $\sin x$ is $\cos x$, so try differentiating $\sin(ax)$.

If $F(x) = \sin(ax)$, then by the chain rule, $F'(x) = a\cos(ax)$.

Hence

$$\int \cos(ax)\,dx = \frac{1}{a}\int a\cos(ax)\,dx = \frac{1}{a}\sin ax + c,$$

where $c$ is an arbitrary constant.

A similar method can be used to show that

$$\int \sin(ax)\,dx = -\frac{1}{a}\cos(ax) + c, \quad \text{and} \quad \int e^{ax}\,dx = \frac{1}{a}e^{ax} + c.$$

**Activity 43**   *Integrating trigonometric functions*

(a)  Find $\displaystyle\int \sec^2(ax)\,dx$.

(b)  Differentiate $y = \tan^{-1}\left(\dfrac{x}{a}\right)$. Hence find

$$\int \frac{1}{a^2 + x^2}\,dx.$$

## 6.2   Definite integration

> For more detail on the topics covered in this subsection, refer to
> Sections 1 and 2 of MST124 Unit 8.

In this subsection we consider the problem of finding the area between a
graph and the $x$-axis.

We make the following definitions. Suppose that $f$ is a continuous function
and $a$ and $b$ are numbers in its domain. First suppose that $b$ is greater
than $a$.

If the graph of $f$ does not cross or touch the $x$-axis between $x = a$ and
$x = b$ (except possibly at $x = a$ or $x = b$), then the **signed area** between
the graph of $f$ and the $x$-axis from $x = a$ to $x = b$ is the area of the region
between the graph of $f$ and the $x$-axis from $x = a$ to $x = b$, with a plus or
minus sign according to whether this region lies above or below the $x$-axis.
For example, the signed area illustrated in Figure 35 has a positive value.

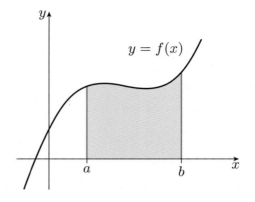

**Figure 35**   The signed area between the graph of $f$ and the $x$-axis from $x = a$ to $x = b$

Now suppose that the graph of $f$ crosses or touches the $x$-axis between $x = a$ and $x = b$, so that there are two or more individual regions between the graph of $f$ and the $x$-axis between $x = a$ and $x = b$, each of which lies entirely above or below the $x$-axis. Then the **signed area** between the graph of $f$ and the $x$-axis from $x = a$ to $x = b$ is the sum of the signed areas of these regions.

An example is given in Figure 36, which shows the graph of the sine function from $x = 0$ to $x = 2\pi$. The signed area from $0$ to $\pi$ is positive and the signed area from $\pi$ to $2\pi$ is negative. From the symmetry of this graph, the area above the $x$-axis is equal to the area below the $x$-axis. So the total signed area from $0$ to $2\pi$ is zero.

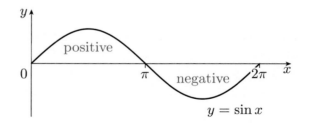

**Figure 36**   The signed areas of $y = \sin x$ from $x = 0$ to $x = 2\pi$

If $b$ is less than $a$, then the **signed area** between the graph of $f$ and the $x$-axis from $x = a$ to $x = b$ is the *negative* of the signed area between the graph of $f$ and the $x$-axis from $x = b$ to $x = a$. If $a = b$, then the signed area is zero.

This idea of the signed area is used to define the definite integral of a continuous function, as in the box below.

## Definite integrals

Suppose that $f$ is a continuous function, and $a$ and $b$ are numbers in its domain. The signed area between the graph of $f$ and the $x$-axis from $x = a$ to $x = b$ is called the **definite integral** of $f$ from $a$ to $b$, and is denoted by

$$\int_a^b f(x)\,\mathrm{d}x.$$

Not the meaning of a definite integral.

For example, since the signed area in Figure 36 is zero, we have

$$\int_0^{2\pi} \sin x\,\mathrm{d}x = 0.$$

The numbers $a$ and $b$ in the notation

$$\int_a^b f(x)\,\mathrm{d}x$$

are called the **lower** and **upper limits of integration**, respectively. Note that, because of the way we have defined the signed area, the definition of the definite integral applies whether the value of $a$ is less than, equal to or greater than the value of $b$, and in particular

$$\int_b^a f(x)\,\mathrm{d}x = -\int_a^b f(x)\,\mathrm{d}x.$$

By the fundamental theorem of calculus, if $F$ is an antiderivative of $f$, then the definite integral

$$\int_a^b f(x)\,\mathrm{d}x$$

can be evaluated by calculating the change in the value of $F(x)$ from $x = a$ to $x = b$, as stated below.

## Fundamental theorem of calculus

Suppose that $f$ is a continuous function whose domain includes the numbers $a$ and $b$, and that $F$ is an antiderivative of $f$. Then

$$\int_a^b f(x)\,\mathrm{d}x = F(b) - F(a).$$

For any function $F$, the expression

$$F(b) - F(a)$$

can be written in **square bracket notation** as follows:

$$\left[F(x)\right]_a^b = F(b) - F(a).$$

As an example of the fundamental theorem of calculus, consider again the function $f(x) = \sin x$ whose graph is shown in Figure 36. An antiderivative of $f$ is $F(x) = -\cos x$, so

$$\int_0^{2\pi} \sin x \, \mathrm{d}x = \Big[ -\cos x \Big]_0^{2\pi} = -\cos(2\pi) + \cos 0 = -1 + 1 = 0,$$

which agrees with the calculation above using signed areas.

The next example and activity will give you practice in evaluating definite integrals using the fundamental theorem of calculus.

**Example 20**   *Evaluating a definite integral*

Evaluate the definite integral

$$\int_1^4 \left( \frac{x+1}{\sqrt{x}} \right) \mathrm{d}x.$$

**Solution**

🔍 Manipulate the integrand to get it into a form that you can integrate. 💬

$$\int_1^4 \left( \frac{x+1}{\sqrt{x}} \right) \mathrm{d}x = \int_1^4 \left( \sqrt{x} + \frac{1}{\sqrt{x}} \right) \mathrm{d}x$$

$$= \int_1^4 \left( x^{\frac{1}{2}} + x^{-\frac{1}{2}} \right) \mathrm{d}x.$$

🔍 Now apply the fundamental theorem of calculus, and evaluate the result. 💬

$$\int_1^4 \left( x^{\frac{1}{2}} + x^{-\frac{1}{2}} \right) \mathrm{d}x = \left[ \frac{2}{3} x^{\frac{3}{2}} + 2x^{\frac{1}{2}} \right]_1^4$$

$$= \left( \frac{2}{3}(4)^{\frac{3}{2}} + 2(4)^{\frac{1}{2}} \right) - \left( \frac{2}{3}(1)^{\frac{3}{2}} + 2(1)^{\frac{1}{2}} \right)$$

$$= \left( \frac{2}{3} \times 8 + 2 \times 2 \right) - \left( \frac{2}{3} \times 1 + 2 \times 1 \right)$$

$$= \frac{20}{3}.$$

**Activity 44**    *Evaluating definite integrals*

Evaluate the following definite integrals. Give exact answers.

(a) $\displaystyle\int_0^{\pi/4} 3\sin 4x \, dx$      (b) $\displaystyle\int_{-1}^{0} e^t(1 + e^{2t}) \, dt$      (c) $\displaystyle\int_1^{e} \frac{1}{2r} \, dr$

## 6.3  Using integration to solve some practical problems

> For more detail on the topics covered in this subsection, refer to Section 5 of MST124 Unit 7.

In Subsection 5.4 of this unit you saw that, if you have a formula for the displacement $s$ of an object along a straight line in terms of the time $t$, then the object's velocity $v$ is given by

$$\frac{ds}{dt},$$

and its acceleration $a$ is given by

$$\frac{dv}{dt}, \quad \text{that is, by } \frac{d^2s}{dt^2}.$$

So if you know the acceleration $a$ of an object moving along a straight line in terms of the time $t$, then you can integrate $a$ to obtain a formula for $v$, and then integrate $v$ to obtain a formula for $s$. You can work out the constants of integration by substituting the values of $v$ and $s$ at a particular time into the formulas for $v$ and $s$ respectively.

For example, suppose that an object moves along a straight line with constant acceleration $a = 10 \, \text{m s}^{-2}$, and that $v = 0 \, \text{m s}^{-1}$ when $t = 0$ s.

Then $\dfrac{dv}{dt} = 10$, so $v = 10t + c$, where $c$ is an arbitrary constant.

But we know that $v = 0$ when $t = 0$, so substituting these values into the formula for $v$ gives

$$0 = 10 \times 0 + c,$$

so $c = 0$.

Hence the formula for the velocity $v$ of the object in terms of time is

$$v = 10t.$$

The next activity asks you to find the displacement of an object from its acceleration, given its velocity and displacement at the start of the motion.

**Activity 45**   *Using integration to investigate motion along a straight line*

Suppose that a ball is thrown vertically upwards with initial speed $10\,\mathrm{m\,s^{-1}}$, from a point that is two metres above the ground. Assume that its subsequent motion is modelled as having a constant acceleration of $-9.8\,\mathrm{m\,s^{-2}}$, where the positive direction along the line of motion is upwards.

Let the acceleration, velocity and displacement of the ball at time $t$ (in seconds) after it was thrown be $a$ (in $\mathrm{m\,s^{-2}}$), $v$ (in $\mathrm{m\,s^{-1}}$), and $s$ (in m), respectively, where displacement is measured from the ground.

(a) Find an equation that expresses $v$ in terms of $t$ (with no arbitrary constant).

(b) Hence find an equation that expresses $s$ in terms of $t$ (with no arbitrary constant).

(c) Use the formulas that you found in parts (a) and (b) to find the velocity and the displacement of the ball half a second after it was thrown.

(d) Use the formula that you found in part (b) to determine how long it takes for the ball to fall back to the ground.

(Hint: at the time when the ball has fallen back to the ground, what is the value of $s$?)

# 7 The computer algebra system

The computer algebra system (CAS) used in MST125 is the same one that is used in MST124.

In MST125, it is assumed that you have already learned to use the CAS to perform the following tasks:

- open, edit, save and print files
- use variables, functions and lists
- manipulate algebraic expressions
- solve equations
- plot graphs
- differentiate and integrate functions.

You can revise these skills in the following activity.

**Activity 46** *Using the computer algebra system*

If the CAS is not already installed on your computer, then follow the instructions in Section 1 of the MST125 *Computer algebra guide* to install it.

Then, if you have not used the CAS before, or have not used it recently, work through Sections 2 and 3 of the MST125 *Computer algebra guide* thoroughly.

Alternatively, if you are familiar with the CAS, then skim through Sections 2 and 3 of the MST125 *Computer algebra guide* quickly, and try the activities in Section 3 to check your skills, revising them more thoroughly as necessary. You may find it helpful to refer to the reference guide at the back of the *Computer algebra guide* to remind yourself of the syntax needed.

You have now finished revising the key techniques needed for MST125. We hope that you will enjoy studying the module!

# Learning outcomes

After studying this unit, you should be able to:

- work with functions, composite functions and inverses
- translate and scale graphs of functions
- solve trigonometric equations
- establish and use trigonometric identities
- represent vectors both geometrically and using components
- add and subtract vectors and simplify vector expressions
- calculate the scalar product of two vectors
- add, subtract and multiply matrices
- find the inverse of an invertible matrix
- differentiate products, quotients and composite functions
- find the stationary points of a function
- understand rates of change
- find indefinite and definite integrals
- use the computer algebra system.

# Solutions to activities

## Solution to Activity 1

(a) The graph of $f(x) = -2(x + 1)^2 + 8$ can be obtained by translating the graph of $g(x)$ by 1 unit to the left, then scaling by a factor of 2 in the $y$-direction, then reflecting in the $x$-axis, and finally translating 8 units upwards in the $y$-direction. (Other sequences are possible.)

The vertex of $g(x)$ is at $(0, 0)$. Applying the translations and scaling to the point $(0, 0)$ gives the point $(-1, 8)$. Hence the vertex of $f(x)$ is at $(-1, 8)$.

When $x = 0$, we have $y = -2(0 + 1)^2 + 8 = 6$. So the graph crosses the $y$-axis at $(0, 6)$.

When $y = 0$, we have $-2(x + 1)^2 + 8 = 0$. So $(x + 1)^2 = 4$ and $x + 1 = \pm 2$. Hence $x = -3$ or $x = 1$, so the graph crosses the $x$-axis at $(-3, 0)$ and at $(1, 0)$.

The graph of $f$ is shown below.

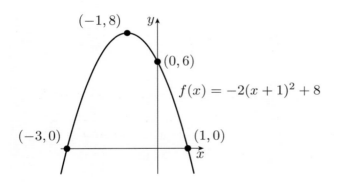

(See Subsection 1.2 for relevant material.)

(b) The function $h$ has the same rule as the function $f$ from part (a), but is only defined when $-2 < x \leq 1$.

When $x = -2$, $f(-2) = -2(-2 + 1)^2 + 8 = 6$, but $h$ is not defined at $x = -2$ so the point $(-2, 6)$ is not part of its graph (indicated by a hollow dot).

From the graph of the function $f$ in part (a), $h(x)$ takes its minimum value of 0 when $x = 1$ and its maximum value of 8 when $x = -1$. Hence the image set of $h$ is $[0, 8]$.

The graph of $h$ and its image set are shown below.

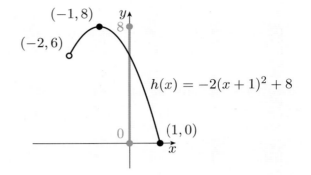

(See Subsection 1.1 for relevant material.)

(c) No, $h$ does not have an inverse function because it is not one-to-one for values of $x$ in the interval $(-2, 0)$.

(See Subsection 1.4 for relevant material.)

(d)
$$y = 3x - 2$$
$$y + 2 = 3x$$
$$x = \tfrac{1}{3}(y + 2).$$

Hence the rule for the inverse function is
$$k^{-1}(x) = \tfrac{1}{3}(x + 2).$$

The graphs of $k$ and its inverse $k^{-1}$ are shown below; the axes have the same scale.

(See Subsection 1.4 for relevant material.)

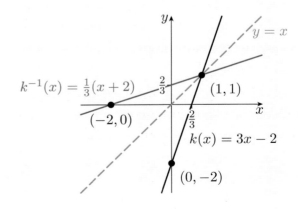

(e) (i)  $k \circ k(x) = k(3x - 2)$
$$= 3(3x - 2) - 2$$
$$= 9x - 8.$$

(ii)  $f \circ k(x) = f(3x - 2)$
$$= -2\left((3x - 2) + 1\right)^2 + 8$$
$$= -2(3x - 1)^2 + 8$$
$$= -2(9x^2 - 6x + 1) + 8$$
$$= -18x^2 + 12x + 6.$$

(iii)  $k \circ f(x) = k(-2(x + 1)^2 + 8)$
$$= 3(-2(x + 1)^2 + 8) - 2$$
$$= -6(x + 1)^2 + 22$$
$$= -6x^2 - 12x + 16.$$

(See Subsection 1.3 for relevant material.)

## Solution to Activity 2

(a) When $x = \frac{3}{2}$, $2x - 3 = 0$. It is therefore not possible to work out $f(\frac{3}{2})$, so this rule cannot be used to specify a function with domain $\mathbb{R}$.

(b) Each input value $t$ has two output values $t \pm 3$, so this rule cannot be used to specify a function.

(c) When $p = 0$, $s(p) = s(0) = \sqrt{-12}$, which is not defined, so it is not possible to specify a function with this rule whose codomain is $\mathbb{R}$. Indeed, $s(p)$ is not defined whenever $-2 < p < 6$.

## Solution to Activity 3

(a) The expression under the square root sign has to be non-negative, so the domain is the set of all values of $t$ such that $t \geq 4$; that is, the interval $[4, \infty)$. In set notation, the domain can be written $t \in [4, \infty)$.

(b) Factorising the denominator gives
$$u^2 - 4 = (u + 2)(u - 2).$$
So the denominator is zero when $u = -2$ or $u = 2$, and $h(u)$ cannot be worked out for these values of $u$. Hence the domain is $u \in \mathbb{R}, u \neq -2, u \neq 2$. In set notation, the domain can be written as
$$u \in (-\infty, -2) \cup (-2, 2) \cup (2, \infty).$$

## Solution to Activity 4

(a) Since $f$ is a linear function with a restricted domain, its graph is part of a straight line.

When $x = -0.5$,
$$f(x) = f(-0.5) = 3 \times (-0.5) - 4 = -5.5,$$
but since $x = -0.5$ is not in the domain, the point $(-0.5, -5.5)$ does not lie on the graph of $f$.

When $x = 2$, $f(x) = f(2) = 3 \times 2 - 4 = 2$, and since $x = 2$ is in the domain, the point $(2, 2)$ does lie on the graph.

The graph of $f$ is shown below. The image set $(-5.5, 2]$ is marked on the $y$-axis.

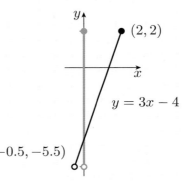

(b) (i)   From the graph, the image set is $(0, 4]$.

(ii)   The minimum value occurs at $x = 2$ and the maximum value occurs at $x = -1$, so the image set is $[f(2), f(-1)]$.

Now
$$f(2) = 2 \times 2^3 - 3 \times 2^2 - 12 \times 2 + 4$$
$$= -16,$$
and
$$f(-1) = 2 \times (-1)^3 - 3 \times (-1)^2$$
$$- 12 \times (-1) + 4$$
$$= 11.$$
Hence the image set is $[-16, 11]$.

**Solution to Activity 5**

(a) (i)   The graph of
$$g(x) = \frac{1}{x} + 2$$
can be obtained by translating the graph of $f(x) = 1/x$ by 2 units upwards.

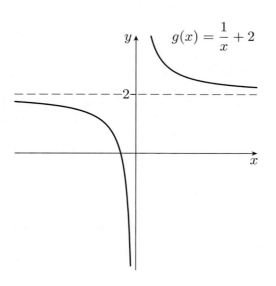

(ii)   The graph of
$$h(x) = \frac{1}{x+2}$$
can be obtained by translating the graph of $f(x) = 1/x$ by 2 units to the left.

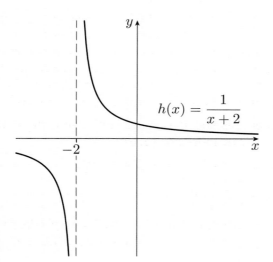

(b)   Put the right-hand side over a common denominator to give
$$\frac{1}{x-2} + 3 = \frac{1 + 3(x-2)}{x-2}$$
$$= \frac{3x - 5}{x - 2}.$$
Hence the graph of
$$q(x) = \frac{3x - 5}{x - 2}$$
can be obtained by translating the graph of $f(x) = 1/x$ by 2 units to the right and 3 units up.

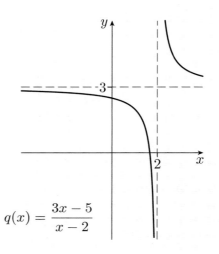

**Solution to Activity 6**

(a) (i)   The function $g(x) = -3e^x$ is of the form $cf(x)$ where $c = -3$ and $f(x) = e^x$.

So the graph of $g(x) = -3e^x$ can be obtained by scaling the graph of $f(x) = e^x$ by a factor of 3 in the $y$-direction and then reflecting it in the $x$-axis.

(ii)   The function $h(x) = e^{2x}$ is of the form $f\left(\frac{x}{c}\right)$ where $c = \frac{1}{2}$ and $f(x) = e^x$.

So the graph of $h(x) = e^{2x}$ can be obtained by scaling the graph of $f(x) = e^x$ by a factor of $\frac{1}{2}$ in the $x$-direction.

(iii) The function $k(x) = e^{x-1} = e^x \times e^{-1}$ is of the form $cf(x)$ where $c = 1/e$ and $f(x) = e^x$.

So the graph of $k(x) = e^{x-1}$ can be obtained by scaling the graph of $f(x) = e^x$ by a factor of $1/e$ in the $y$-direction. This graph can also be obtained by translating the graph of $f(x) = e^x$ by 1 unit to the right.

(b) (i) The equation of the scaled graph is
$$y = \tfrac{1}{3}x^2.$$

(ii) The equation of the scaled graph is
$$y = \ln\left(\frac{x}{2}\right) = \ln x - \ln 2.$$

(iii) The equation of the scaled graph is
$$y = \cos\left(\frac{x}{-1/2}\right) = \cos(-2x) = \cos(2x).$$

(iv) The equation of the scaled graph is
$$y = -\tfrac{2}{3}e^x.$$

## Solution to Activity 7

(a) Translate the graph of $y = x^3$ by 1 unit to the right to obtain the graph of $y = (x-1)^3$. Then translate this graph 2 units downwards to obtain the graph of $y = (x-1)^3 - 2$.

Under these translations, the point $P$ at $(0,0)$ moves to $(1, -2)$.

When $x = 0$, $y = (0-1)^3 - 2 = -3$, so the $y$-intercept is $-3$. The graph is shown below.

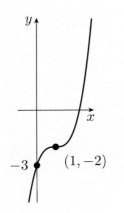

(b) Translate the graph of $y = x^3$ by 2 units to the left to obtain the graph of $y = (x+2)^3$. Then scale this graph by a factor of $\frac{1}{8}$ in the vertical direction to obtain the graph of
$$y = \frac{(x+2)^3}{8}.$$

Under this translation and scaling, the point $P$ at $(0,0)$ moves to $(-2, 0)$.

Alternatively, you could note that
$$y = \left(\frac{x+2}{2}\right)^3.$$

So the graph can also be obtained by scaling the graph of $y = x^3$ by a factor of 2 horizontally to obtain the graph of $y = (x/2)^3$, and then translating this graph by 2 units to the left.

When $x = 0$,
$$y = \frac{(0+2)^3}{8} = 1,$$
so the $y$-intercept is 1. The graph is shown below.

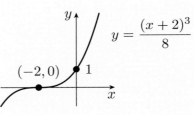

(c) Note that $(2-x)^3 = (-1)^3(x-2)^3$, so $y = -(x-2)^3$. To obtain the graph of $y = -(x-2)^3$, translate the graph of $y = x^3$ by 2 units to the right to obtain the graph of $y = (x-2)^3$, then reflect this graph in the $x$-axis to obtain the graph of $y = -(x-2)^3$.

Under this translation and reflection, the point $P$ at $(0,0)$ moves to $(2, 0)$.

Alternatively, you could note that
$$y = \left(\frac{x-2}{-1}\right)^3.$$

So the graph can also be obtained by reflecting the graph of $y = x^3$ in the $y$-axis to obtain the graph of
$$y = (-x)^3 = \left(\frac{x}{-1}\right)^3,$$

then translating this graph by 2 units to the right to obtain the graph of

$$y = \left(\frac{x-2}{-1}\right)^3.$$

When $x = 0$, $y = (2-0)^3 = 8$, so the $y$-intercept is 8. The graph is shown below.

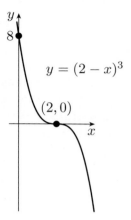

## Solution to Activity 8

(a) $(f \circ g)(x) = f(g(x))$
$$= f(4 - x^2)$$
$$= 2(4 - x^2) - 1$$
$$= -2x^2 + 7.$$

(b) $(g \circ f)(x) = g(f(x))$
$$= g(2x - 1)$$
$$= 4 - (2x - 1)^2$$
$$= 4 - (4x^2 - 4x + 1)$$
$$= -4x^2 + 4x + 3.$$

(c) $(g \circ f \circ f)(x) = g(f(f(x)))$
$$= g(f(2x - 1))$$
$$= g(2(2x - 1) - 1)$$
$$= g(4x - 3)$$
$$= 4 - (4x - 3)^2$$
$$= 4 - (16x^2 - 24x + 9)$$
$$= -16x^2 + 24x - 5.$$

## Solution to Activity 9

(a) The graph shows that $f$ is decreasing on its whole domain $[-3, 1]$, so it is one-to-one and therefore has an inverse function. From the graph, the image set of $f$ is $[1, 13]$, so the domain of $f^{-1}$ is $[1, 13]$. The equation $y = 4 - 3x$ can be rearranged as follows.
$$y = 4 - 3x$$
$$3x = 4 - y$$
$$x = \frac{4 - y}{3}.$$

Hence the rule of $f^{-1}(y) = \dfrac{4 - y}{3}$, that is, $f^{-1}(x) = \dfrac{4 - x}{3}$. So the inverse function of $f$ is
$$f^{-1}(x) = \frac{4 - x}{3} \quad (x \in [1, 13]).$$

The graphs of $f$ and $f^{-1}$ on axes with equal scales are shown below.

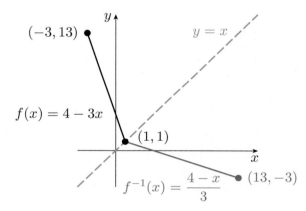

(b) The graph shows that $g$ is not one-to-one on its whole domain, since it is possible to draw horizontal lines which meet the graph more than once. So $g$ does not have an inverse function.

Alternatively, you could note that
$$g(-1) = g(1) = g(2) = 0,$$
so $g$ is not one-to-one and hence does not have an inverse function.

## Solution to Activity 10

(a)

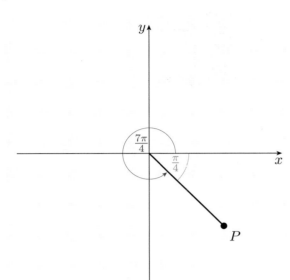

The point $P$ on the unit circle associated with the angle $7\pi/4$ lies in the fourth quadrant (see the figure above). Hence the cosine of the angle is positive and the sine and tangent are negative. (You can see this by using the ASTC diagram.)

The sizes of the sine, cosine and tangent of $7\pi/4$ are the same as the sizes of the sine, cosine and tangent of $\pi/4$, the acute angle between $OP$ and the $x$-axis.

Hence
$$\sin\left(\frac{7\pi}{4}\right) = -\sin\left(\frac{\pi}{4}\right) = -\frac{1}{\sqrt{2}}.$$
Similarly,
$$\cos\left(\frac{7\pi}{4}\right) = +\cos\left(\frac{\pi}{4}\right) = \frac{1}{\sqrt{2}}$$
and
$$\tan\left(\frac{7\pi}{4}\right) = -\tan\left(\frac{\pi}{4}\right) = -1.$$

(See Subsection 2.1 for relevant material.)

(b) The sine of $\theta$ is negative, so the ASTC diagram tells us that $\theta$ must be a third- or fourth-quadrant angle. The diagram below shows the associated acute angle $\phi$ with the $x$-axis for each of these possibilities.

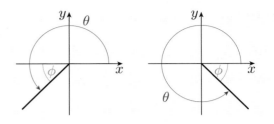

Here
$$\sin\theta = -\frac{1}{\sqrt{2}},$$
so
$$\sin\phi = \frac{1}{\sqrt{2}},$$
and hence
$$\phi = \sin^{-1}\left(\frac{1}{\sqrt{2}}\right) = 45°.$$
So, using the diagram, the solutions are
$$\theta = 180° + \phi = 180° + 45° = 225°$$
and
$$\theta = 360° - \phi = 360° - 45° = 315°.$$
(See Subsection 2.1 for relevant material.)

(c) The graph of $\cos\theta$ for $-\pi < \theta < \pi$ is shown below.

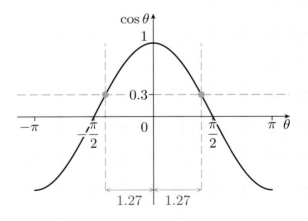

The inverse cosine function can be used to find the solution that lies in the interval $[0, \pi]$. This solution is $\theta = \cos^{-1}(0.3)$, which is 1.27 radians (to 3 s.f.).

Using the symmetry of the graph, the other solution is $-1.27$ radians (to 3 s.f.).

(See Subsection 2.1 for relevant material.)

(d) The most convenient trigonometric identity to use here is
$$\sin^2 \theta = \tfrac{1}{2}(1 - \cos(2\theta)).$$
Substituting $\cos(2\theta) = \tfrac{3}{5}$ gives
$$\begin{aligned}\sin^2 \theta &= \tfrac{1}{2}\left(1 - \tfrac{3}{5}\right) \\ &= \tfrac{1}{2} \times \tfrac{2}{5} \\ &= \tfrac{1}{5}.\end{aligned}$$
Hence $\sin \theta = \pm\sqrt{\tfrac{1}{5}}$.

The angle $\theta$ is acute, so $\sin \theta$ is positive and hence
$$\sin \theta = \sqrt{\tfrac{1}{5}} = \frac{1}{\sqrt{5}}.$$

## Solution to Activity 11

(a) The point on the unit circle which corresponds to an angle of $-3\pi$ has coordinates $(-1, 0)$. So $\cos(-3\pi)$ is the $x$-coordinate of this point, that is $-1$.

(b) The angle $2\pi/3$ lies in the second quadrant so, from the ASTC diagram, $\tan\left(\dfrac{2\pi}{3}\right)$ is negative. From the diagram below, the associated acute angle with the $x$-axis is $\pi/3$.

Hence, using the special angles table,
$$\tan\left(\frac{2\pi}{3}\right) = -\tan\left(\frac{\pi}{3}\right) = -\sqrt{3}.$$

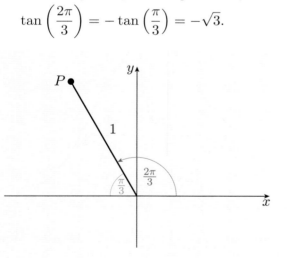

(c) The angle $-3\pi/4$ lies in the third quadrant so, from the ASTC diagram, $\sin\left(-\dfrac{3\pi}{4}\right)$ is negative. From the diagram below, the associated acute angle with the $x$-axis is $\pi/4$.

Hence, using the special angles table,
$$\sin\left(-\frac{3\pi}{4}\right) = -\sin\left(\frac{\pi}{4}\right) = -\frac{1}{\sqrt{2}}.$$

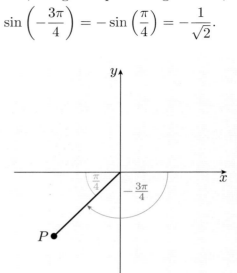

## Solution to Activity 12

(a) The tangent of $\theta$ is negative so, from the ASTC diagram, $\theta$ is a second- or fourth-quadrant angle. The two possibilities are shown in the diagrams below, which also show the corresponding acute angle $\phi$ with the $x$-axis.

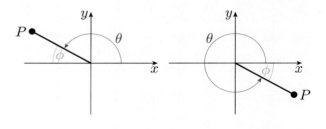

Now
$$\tan \theta = -\frac{1}{\sqrt{3}}, \quad \text{so} \quad \tan \phi = \frac{1}{\sqrt{3}}.$$
Therefore, from the special angles table, $\phi = \dfrac{\pi}{6}$.

Hence, from the above diagrams, the solutions are

$$\theta = \pi - \phi = \pi - \frac{\pi}{6} = \frac{5\pi}{6}$$

and

$$\theta = 2\pi - \phi = 2\pi - \frac{\pi}{6} = \frac{11\pi}{6}.$$

(b) The sine of $\theta$ is negative so, from the ASTC diagram, $\theta$ is a third- or fourth-quadrant angle. The two possibilities are shown in the diagrams below, which also show the corresponding acute angle $\phi$ with the $x$-axis.

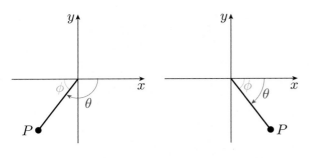

Here

$$\sin\theta = -0.8, \quad \text{so} \quad \sin\phi = 0.8.$$

Therefore, using a calculator,

$$\phi = \sin^{-1}(0.8) = 53.130\ldots^{\circ}.$$

Hence

$$\theta = -(180^{\circ} - \phi) = -(180^{\circ} - 53.130\ldots^{\circ})$$
$$= -126.870\ldots^{\circ}$$

and

$$\theta = -\phi = -53.130\ldots^{\circ}.$$

So the solutions are $-53^{\circ}$ and $-127^{\circ}$, to the nearest degree.

## Solution to Activity 13

(a) The graph of the sine function on the interval $[-180^{\circ}, 180^{\circ}]$ is shown below. The graph also shows the horizontal line at height 0.2 and the crossing points.

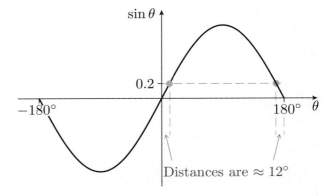

Distances are $\approx 12^{\circ}$

One solution (the solution between $-90^{\circ}$ and $90^{\circ}$) is

$$\theta = \sin^{-1}(0.2) = 11.536\ldots^{\circ}.$$

From the symmetry of the graph, the other solution is

$$\theta = 180^{\circ} - 11.536\ldots^{\circ} = 168.463\ldots^{\circ}.$$

So the solutions are $12^{\circ}$ and $168^{\circ}$, to the nearest degree.

(b) The graph of the tangent function on the interval $[-\pi, \pi]$ is shown below. The graph also shows the horizontal line at height $-3$ and the crossing points.

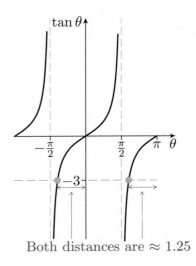

Both distances are $\approx 1.25$

One solution (the solution between $-\pi/2$ and $\pi/2$) is

$$\theta = \tan^{-1}(-3) = -1.249\ldots.$$

From the symmetry of the graph, the other solution is
$$\theta = \pi - 1.249\ldots = 1.892\ldots.$$
So the solutions are $-1.25$ radians and $1.89$ radians (to 3 s.f.).

## Solution to Activity 14

(a)   $\operatorname{cosec}\left(\dfrac{\pi}{3}\right) = \dfrac{1}{\sin\left(\dfrac{\pi}{3}\right)} = \dfrac{1}{\sqrt{3}/2} = \dfrac{2}{\sqrt{3}}$

$\sec\left(\dfrac{\pi}{3}\right) = \dfrac{1}{\cos\left(\dfrac{\pi}{3}\right)} = \dfrac{1}{1/2} = 2$

$\cot\left(\dfrac{\pi}{3}\right) = \dfrac{\cos\left(\dfrac{\pi}{3}\right)}{\sin\left(\dfrac{\pi}{3}\right)} = \dfrac{1/2}{\sqrt{3}/2} = \dfrac{1}{\sqrt{3}}$

(b)   We have
$$g(\theta) = \operatorname{cosec}(2\theta) = \dfrac{1}{\sin(2\theta)}.$$
So, $g(\theta)$ is not defined when $\sin(2\theta) = 0$; that is, $g(\theta)$ is not defined when $2\theta = n\pi$ and hence when $\theta = n\pi/2$, where $n$ is an integer.

## Solution to Activity 15

(a)   Dividing both sides of the identity $\sin^2\theta + \cos^2\theta = 1$ by $\cos^2\theta$ gives
$$\dfrac{\sin^2\theta}{\cos^2\theta} + 1 = \dfrac{1}{\cos^2\theta};$$
that is,
$$\tan^2\theta + 1 = \sec^2\theta.$$

(b)   Dividing both sides of the identity $\sin^2\theta + \cos^2\theta = 1$ by $\sin^2\theta$ gives
$$1 + \dfrac{\cos^2\theta}{\sin^2\theta} = \dfrac{1}{\sin^2\theta};$$
that is,
$$1 + \cot^2\theta = \operatorname{cosec}^2\theta.$$

## Solution to Activity 16

Using the double-angle identity for cosine,
$$\begin{aligned}
\cos(2\phi) &= 2\cos^2\phi - 1 \\
&= 2 \times \left(\tfrac{1}{2}\right)^2 - 1 \\
&= -\tfrac{1}{2}.
\end{aligned}$$

## Solution to Activity 17

(a)   Let $\mathbf{a}$ be the first displacement of 4 km on a bearing of $210°$, and $\mathbf{b}$ be the second displacement of 7 km on a bearing of $290°$. The resultant displacement of the hiker is $\mathbf{a} + \mathbf{b}$, as shown below.

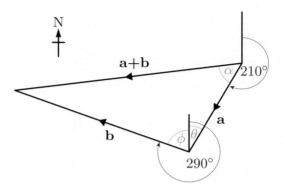

We know that $|\mathbf{a}| = 4$ and $|\mathbf{b}| = 7$.

Since alternate angles are equal, the angle $\theta$ marked on the diagram at the tip of $\mathbf{a}$ is $210° - 180° = 30°$.

The angle $\phi$ marked at the tail of $\mathbf{b}$ is given by $\phi = 360° - 290° = 70°$.

So the bottom angle of the triangle is $\theta + \phi = 30° + 70° = 100°$.

The distance the hiker has travelled from her starting point is $|\mathbf{a} + \mathbf{b}|$. Applying the cosine rule gives
$$|\mathbf{a} + \mathbf{b}|^2 = |\mathbf{a}|^2 + |\mathbf{b}|^2 - 2|\mathbf{a}||\mathbf{b}|\cos(\theta + \phi),$$
so
$$\begin{aligned}
|\mathbf{a} + \mathbf{b}| &= \sqrt{4^2 + 7^2 - 2 \times 4 \times 7 \times \cos 100°} \\
&= 8.644\ldots.
\end{aligned}$$

The bearing of the hiker's final position from her starting point is $210° + \alpha$, where $\alpha$ is the angle shown on the diagram.

The angle $\alpha$ can be found by using the sine rule:
$$\dfrac{|\mathbf{b}|}{\sin\alpha} = \dfrac{|\mathbf{a} + \mathbf{b}|}{\sin(\theta + \phi)}$$
$$\sin\alpha = \dfrac{|\mathbf{b}|\sin(\theta + \phi)}{|\mathbf{a} + \mathbf{b}|} = \dfrac{7\sin 100°}{8.644\ldots}.$$
Now,
$$\sin^{-1}\left(\dfrac{7\sin 100°}{8.644\ldots}\right) = 52.88\ldots°.$$

So $\alpha = 52.88\ldots^\circ$ or
$\alpha = 180^\circ - 52.88\ldots^\circ = 127.11\ldots^\circ$.

But $|\mathbf{b}| < |\mathbf{a} + \mathbf{b}|$, so we expect $\alpha < \theta + \phi$; that is, $\alpha < 100^\circ$. So $\alpha = 52.88\ldots^\circ$ and hence the bearing of $\mathbf{a} + \mathbf{b}$ is

$$210^\circ + 52.88\ldots^\circ = 262.88\ldots^\circ.$$

Hence the hiker has travelled a distance of $8.6\,\text{km}$ (to 2 s.f.) from her starting point, on a bearing of $263^\circ$ (to the nearest degree).

(See Subsection 3.1 for relevant material.)

(b) (i) $\quad \mathbf{a} + 2\mathbf{b} - 0.5\mathbf{c} = (\mathbf{i} - \mathbf{j}) + 2(-2\mathbf{i} + \mathbf{j})$
$$\phantom{\mathbf{a} + 2\mathbf{b} - 0.5\mathbf{c} =} - 0.5(6\mathbf{i} - 4\mathbf{j})$$
$$= \mathbf{i} - \mathbf{j} - 4\mathbf{i} + 2\mathbf{j} - 3\mathbf{i} + 2\mathbf{j}$$
$$= -6\mathbf{i} + 3\mathbf{j}.$$

The magnitude of this vector is
$$\sqrt{(-6)^2 + 3^2} = \sqrt{45}$$
$$= 3\sqrt{5} = 6.7 \text{ (to 2 s.f.)}.$$

The diagram below shows the direction of the vector.

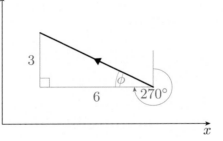

From the diagram, $\tan\phi = \frac{3}{6} = \frac{1}{2}$, so
$$\phi = \tan^{-1}\left(\tfrac{1}{2}\right) = 27^\circ,$$
to the nearest degree. Hence the bearing is $270^\circ + 27^\circ = 297^\circ$, to the nearest degree.

(ii) $\quad 2\begin{pmatrix} -3 \\ 4 \end{pmatrix} - \begin{pmatrix} 2 \\ 5 \end{pmatrix} + 3\begin{pmatrix} 0 \\ -2 \end{pmatrix} = \begin{pmatrix} -8 \\ -3 \end{pmatrix}.$

The magnitude of this vector is
$$\sqrt{(-8)^2 + (-3)^2} = \sqrt{73} = 8.5 \text{ (to 2 s.f.)}.$$

The diagram below shows the direction of the vector.

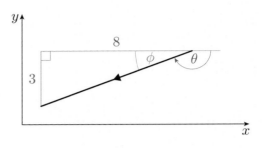

From the diagram, $\tan\phi = \frac{3}{8}$, so
$$\phi = \tan^{-1}\left(\tfrac{3}{8}\right) = 21^\circ,$$
to the nearest degree. Hence the angle $\theta$ that the vector makes with the positive $x$-axis is $-(180^\circ - 21^\circ) = -159^\circ$, to the nearest degree.

(See Subsection 3.2 for relevant material.)

(c) The component form of the vector $\mathbf{p}$ is given by
$$\mathbf{p} = 5\cos(-130^\circ)\mathbf{i} + 5\sin(-130^\circ)\mathbf{j}$$
$$= -3.21\mathbf{i} - 3.83\mathbf{j} \text{ (to 3 s.f.)}.$$

(See Subsection 3.2 for relevant material.)

(d) $\mathbf{p} \cdot \mathbf{q} = 2 \times 3 + (-3) \times (-2) + 1 \times 0 = 12.$

$$|\mathbf{p}| = \sqrt{2^2 + (-3)^2 + 1^2} = \sqrt{14},$$
$$|\mathbf{q}| = \sqrt{3^2 + (-2)^2 + 0^2} = \sqrt{13}.$$

So, if $\theta$ is the angle between $\mathbf{p}$ and $\mathbf{q}$, then
$$\cos\theta = \frac{\mathbf{p} \cdot \mathbf{q}}{|\mathbf{p}|\,|\mathbf{q}|} = \frac{12}{\sqrt{14} \times \sqrt{13}} = 0.889\ldots$$
and hence
$$\theta = \cos^{-1}\left(\frac{12}{\sqrt{14} \times \sqrt{13}}\right) = 27.18\ldots^\circ.$$

So the angle between the vectors is $27^\circ$, to the nearest degree.

(See Subsection 3.3 for relevant material.)

## Solution to Activity 18

Denote Milton Keynes by $M$, Nottingham by $N$, and Birmingham by $B$.

We know that $MN = 109\,\text{km}$ and $NB = 75\,\text{km}$.

Since the bearing of $\overrightarrow{MN}$ is $342°$, the acute angle at $M$ between $\overrightarrow{MN}$ and north is $360° - 342° = 18°$.

Since the bearing of $\overrightarrow{NB}$ is $222°$, the acute angle at $N$ between $\overrightarrow{NB}$ and south is $222° - 180° = 42°$.

These angles are shown in the diagram below.

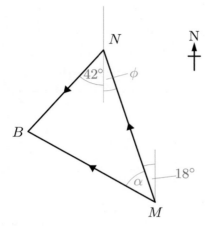

Since alternate angles are equal, the angle marked $\phi$ at the tip of $\overrightarrow{MN}$ is $18°$.

Hence, the angle at the top of the triangle is $42° + 18° = 60°$.

The distance from $M$ to $B$ is $MB$. Applying the cosine rule in triangle $MNB$ gives

$$MB^2 = NB^2 + MN^2 - 2 \times NB \times MN \times \cos 60°,$$

so

$$\begin{aligned} MB &= \sqrt{75^2 + 109^2 - 2 \times 75 \times 109 \times \cos 60°} \\ &= \sqrt{9331} = 96.597\ldots \\ &= 97\,\text{km (to the nearest km)}. \end{aligned}$$

To find the bearing of B from M, we first need to find the angle $\alpha$ shown in the diagram. By the sine rule,

$$\frac{MB}{\sin 60°} = \frac{NB}{\sin \alpha}$$

$$\begin{aligned} \sin \alpha &= \frac{75 \sin 60°}{96.597\ldots} \\ &= 0.6724\ldots \end{aligned}$$

Now

$$\alpha = \sin^{-1}(0.6724\ldots) = 42.252\ldots°,$$

or

$$\alpha = 180° - 42.252\ldots° = 137.748\ldots°.$$

But $NB < MB$, so we expect $\alpha < 42° + \phi = 60°$. Therefore $\alpha = 42.252\ldots°$.

Hence the bearing of $B$ from $M$ is

$$360° - 18° - 42.252\ldots° = 299.747\ldots°.$$

So the magnitude of the displacement of Birmingham from Milton Keynes is $97\,\text{km}$ (to the nearest km) and the bearing is $300°$ (to the nearest degree).

## Solution to Activity 19

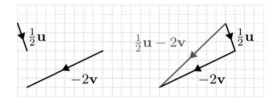

## Solution to Activity 20

(a) $2(\mathbf{a} - \mathbf{b}) - 4(\mathbf{c} - \mathbf{b}) + 3(\mathbf{a} - 2\mathbf{b} + 3\mathbf{c})$
$= 2\mathbf{a} - 2\mathbf{b} - 4\mathbf{c} + 4\mathbf{b} + 3\mathbf{a} - 6\mathbf{b} + 9\mathbf{c}$
$= 5\mathbf{a} - 4\mathbf{b} + 5\mathbf{c}$

(b) (i) $3\mathbf{a} + 2\mathbf{x} = 4\mathbf{a} - \mathbf{c}$
$2\mathbf{x} = \mathbf{a} - \mathbf{c}$
$\mathbf{x} = \frac{1}{2}(\mathbf{a} - \mathbf{c})$

   (ii) $3\mathbf{x} - 2(\mathbf{b} - 2\mathbf{c}) = 4(\mathbf{a} + \mathbf{b}) + 3(\mathbf{b} - 2\mathbf{x})$
$3\mathbf{x} - 2\mathbf{b} + 4\mathbf{c} = 4\mathbf{a} + 4\mathbf{b} + 3\mathbf{b} - 6\mathbf{x}$
$9\mathbf{x} = 4\mathbf{a} + 9\mathbf{b} - 4\mathbf{c}$
$\mathbf{x} = \frac{1}{9}(4\mathbf{a} + 9\mathbf{b} - 4\mathbf{c})$

## Solution to Activity 21

(a) $2\mathbf{p} - \mathbf{q} - 3\mathbf{r}$
$= 2(3\mathbf{i} - 2\mathbf{j}) - (2\mathbf{i} + \mathbf{j}) - 3(-2\mathbf{i} + 3\mathbf{j})$
$= 6\mathbf{i} - 4\mathbf{j} - 2\mathbf{i} - \mathbf{j} + 6\mathbf{i} - 9\mathbf{j}$
$= 10\mathbf{i} - 14\mathbf{j}$

(b) $3\begin{pmatrix} 1 \\ -2 \end{pmatrix} + 2\begin{pmatrix} -1 \\ 2 \end{pmatrix} - 2\begin{pmatrix} 2 \\ 5 \end{pmatrix}$
$= \begin{pmatrix} 3 \times 1 + 2 \times (-1) - 2 \times 2 \\ 3 \times (-2) + 2 \times 2 - 2 \times 5 \end{pmatrix} = \begin{pmatrix} -3 \\ -12 \end{pmatrix}$

(c)  $0.5\mathbf{e} + 1.5\mathbf{f}$
$$= 0.5(3\mathbf{i} - 2\mathbf{j} + \mathbf{k}) + 1.5(3\mathbf{i} - 4\mathbf{j} - 2\mathbf{k})$$
$$= 1.5\mathbf{i} - \mathbf{j} + 0.5\mathbf{k} + 4.5\mathbf{i} - 6\mathbf{j} - 3\mathbf{k}$$
$$= 6\mathbf{i} - 7\mathbf{j} - 2.5\mathbf{k}$$

(d)  $a \begin{pmatrix} 2 \\ -3 \\ 1 \end{pmatrix} + 4 \begin{pmatrix} -a \\ a \\ -2a \end{pmatrix} - 3a \begin{pmatrix} -1 \\ 2 \\ -3 \end{pmatrix}$
$$= \begin{pmatrix} a \times 2 + 4 \times (-a) - 3a \times (-1) \\ a \times (-3) + 4 \times a - 3a \times 2 \\ a \times 1 + 4 \times (-2a) - 3a \times (-3) \end{pmatrix}$$
$$= \begin{pmatrix} a \\ -5a \\ 2a \end{pmatrix}$$

## Solution to Activity 22

(a) (i)  $|3\mathbf{i} - \mathbf{j}| = \sqrt{(3)^2 + (-1)^2}$
$$= \sqrt{10} = 3.2 \text{ (to 1 d.p.).}$$

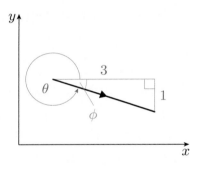

From the diagram,
$$\tan \phi = \tfrac{1}{3},$$
so
$$\phi = \tan^{-1}\left(\tfrac{1}{3}\right) = 18.43\ldots^\circ.$$
Hence the angle, labelled $\theta$, that the vector makes with the positive $x$-direction is
$$360^\circ - 18.43\ldots^\circ = 341.56\ldots^\circ$$
$$= 341.6^\circ \text{ (to 1 d.p.).}$$
Alternatively, you could express the angle with the positive $x$-direction as a negative angle, measured clockwise. In this case, the angle is
$$-\phi = -18.43\ldots^\circ$$
$$= -18.4^\circ \text{ (to 1 d.p.).}$$

(ii)  The magnitude of the vector $\begin{pmatrix} -2 \\ -3 \end{pmatrix}$ is
$$\sqrt{(-2)^2 + (-3)^2} = \sqrt{13} = 3.6 \text{ (to 1 d.p.).}$$

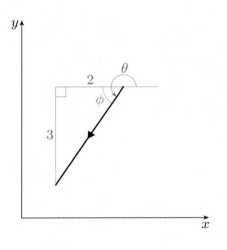

From the diagram,
$$\tan \phi = \tfrac{3}{2},$$
so
$$\phi = \tan^{-1}\left(\tfrac{3}{2}\right) = 56.30\ldots^\circ.$$
Hence the angle, labelled $\theta$, that the vector makes with the positive $x$-direction is
$$180^\circ + 56.30\ldots^\circ = 236.30\ldots^\circ$$
$$= 236.3^\circ \text{ (to 1 d.p.).}$$
Alternatively, you could express the angle with the positive $x$-direction as a negative angle, measured clockwise. In this case, the angle is
$$-(180^\circ - \phi) = -(180^\circ - 56.30\ldots^\circ)$$
$$= -123.70\ldots^\circ$$
$$= -123.7^\circ \text{ (to 1 d.p.).}$$

(b) (i)  $|-\mathbf{i} + 2\mathbf{j} - 4\mathbf{k}| = \sqrt{(-1)^2 + 2^2 + (-4)^2}$
$$= \sqrt{21}.$$

(ii)  $\left| \begin{pmatrix} -2 \\ -1 \\ \sqrt{3} \end{pmatrix} \right| = \sqrt{(-2)^2 + (-1)^2 + (\sqrt{3})^2}$
$$= \sqrt{8}.$$

## Solution to Activity 23

(a)  The component form of $\mathbf{r}$ is
$$\mathbf{r} = 4.5 \cos 165^\circ \mathbf{i} + 4.5 \sin 165^\circ \mathbf{j}$$
$$= -4.3\,\mathbf{i} + 1.2\,\mathbf{j} \text{ (to 2 s.f.).}$$

(b) The vector $\mathbf{w}$ has bearing $190°$, so it makes an angle of $360° - (190° - 90°) = 260°$ with the positive $x$-direction, as shown below.

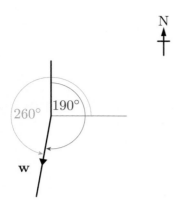

Hence, by the formula for components,
$$\mathbf{w} = 5\cos 260°\mathbf{i} + 5\sin 260°\mathbf{j}$$
$$= -0.87\mathbf{i} - 4.9\mathbf{j} \ (\text{in m s}^{-1}, \text{ to 2 s.f.}).$$

## Solution to Activity 24

(a) (i) If $\mathbf{a}$ and $\mathbf{b}$ are perpendicular, then the angle between them is $90°$. Hence $\mathbf{a} \cdot \mathbf{b} = |\mathbf{a}||\mathbf{b}|\cos 90° = 0$.

Conversely, if $\mathbf{a} \cdot \mathbf{b} = 0$, then $|\mathbf{a}||\mathbf{b}|\cos\theta = 0$. Since $\mathbf{a}$ and $\mathbf{b}$ are non-zero vectors, $|\mathbf{a}| \neq 0$ and $|\mathbf{b}| \neq 0$. Hence $\cos\theta = 0$ and so $\theta = 90°$.

(ii) Let the angle between $\mathbf{a}$ and $\mathbf{b}$ be $\theta$. Then
$$\mathbf{a} \cdot \mathbf{b} = |\mathbf{a}||\mathbf{b}|\cos\theta$$
$$= |\mathbf{b}||\mathbf{a}|\cos\theta$$
$$= \mathbf{b} \cdot \mathbf{a}.$$

(b) If $\mathbf{i}$, $\mathbf{j}$ and $\mathbf{k}$ are the Cartesian unit vectors, then these three vectors are mutually perpendicular. Thus the angle between any pair of these vectors is $90°$, and since $\cos 90° = 0$,
$$\mathbf{i} \cdot \mathbf{j} = \mathbf{j} \cdot \mathbf{k} = \mathbf{k} \cdot \mathbf{i} = 0.$$

The magnitude of a unit vector is 1 and the angle between a vector and itself is zero.

Since $\cos 0° = 1$,
$$\mathbf{i} \cdot \mathbf{i} = \mathbf{j} \cdot \mathbf{j} = \mathbf{k} \cdot \mathbf{k} = 1 \times 1 \times \cos 0° = 1.$$

## Solution to Activity 25

We have
$$\mathbf{a} \cdot \mathbf{b} = 1 \times (-2) + 2 \times 1 + (-1) \times 2 = -2,$$
$$|\mathbf{a}| = \sqrt{1^2 + 2^2 + (-1)^2} = \sqrt{6},$$
$$|\mathbf{b}| = \sqrt{(-2)^2 + 1^2 + 2^2} = \sqrt{9} = 3.$$

So, if $\theta$ is the angle between $\mathbf{a}$ and $\mathbf{b}$, then
$$\cos\theta = \frac{\mathbf{a} \cdot \mathbf{b}}{|\mathbf{a}||\mathbf{b}|} = \frac{-2}{\sqrt{6} \times 3} = -\frac{2 \times \sqrt{6}}{6 \times 3} = -\frac{\sqrt{6}}{9}$$

and hence
$$\theta = \cos^{-1}\left(-\frac{\sqrt{6}}{9}\right) = 105.79\ldots°.$$

So the angle between the vectors is $106°$, to the nearest degree.

## Solution to Activity 26

(a) (i) $\quad 2\mathbf{P} - 3\mathbf{Q} = 2\begin{pmatrix} 0.5 & 1 \\ 1 & 2 \end{pmatrix} - 3\begin{pmatrix} -2 & \frac{1}{4} \\ 3 & -1 \end{pmatrix}$

$\qquad = \begin{pmatrix} 1 & 2 \\ 2 & 4 \end{pmatrix} - \begin{pmatrix} -6 & \frac{3}{4} \\ 9 & -3 \end{pmatrix}$

$\qquad = \begin{pmatrix} 1-(-6) & 2-\frac{3}{4} \\ 2-9 & 4-(-3) \end{pmatrix}$

$\qquad = \begin{pmatrix} 7 & \frac{5}{4} \\ -7 & 7 \end{pmatrix}.$

(See Subsection 4.1 for relevant material.)

(ii) Since $\mathbf{Q}$ is a $2 \times 2$ matrix and $\mathbf{R}$ is a $2 \times 1$ matrix, the number of columns of $\mathbf{Q}$ equals the number of rows of $\mathbf{R}$ and the product $\mathbf{QR}$ can be formed. $\mathbf{QR}$ has size $2 \times 1$.

$\mathbf{QR} = \begin{pmatrix} -2 & \frac{1}{4} \\ 3 & -1 \end{pmatrix}\begin{pmatrix} -1 \\ 3 \end{pmatrix}$

$\quad = \begin{pmatrix} (-2) \times (-1) + \frac{1}{4} \times 3 \\ 3 \times (-1) + (-1) \times 3 \end{pmatrix}$

$\quad = \begin{pmatrix} 2\frac{3}{4} \\ -6 \end{pmatrix}.$

(See Subsection 4.1 for relevant material.)

(iii) $\mathbf{P}^2 = \begin{pmatrix} 0.5 & 1 \\ 1 & 2 \end{pmatrix} \begin{pmatrix} 0.5 & 1 \\ 1 & 2 \end{pmatrix}$

$= \begin{pmatrix} 0.5 \times 0.5 + 1 \times 1 & 0.5 \times 1 + 1 \times 2 \\ 1 \times 0.5 + 2 \times 1 & 1 \times 1 + 2 \times 2 \end{pmatrix}$

$= \begin{pmatrix} 1.25 & 2.5 \\ 2.5 & 5 \end{pmatrix}.$

(See Subsection 4.1 for relevant material.)

(iv) $\det \mathbf{Q} = (-2) \times (-1) - 3 \times \frac{1}{4} = 2 - \frac{3}{4} = \frac{5}{4}.$

Since $\det \mathbf{Q} \neq 0$, the matrix has an inverse.

The inverse is

$\mathbf{Q}^{-1} = \dfrac{1}{(5/4)} \begin{pmatrix} -1 & -\frac{1}{4} \\ -3 & -2 \end{pmatrix}$

$= -\dfrac{1}{5} \begin{pmatrix} 4 & 1 \\ 12 & 8 \end{pmatrix}.$

(See Subsection 4.2 for relevant material.)

(b) (i)   $\mathbf{3P} + \mathbf{2R}$ cannot be calculated because $\mathbf{P}$ and $\mathbf{R}$ are different sizes.

(See Subsection 4.1 for relevant material.)

(ii)  $\mathbf{R}^2$ cannot be calculated because $\mathbf{R}$ is not a square matrix.

(See Subsection 4.1 for relevant material.)

(iii) $\det \mathbf{P} = 0.5 \times 2 - 1 \times 1 = 0$, so $\mathbf{P}$ has no inverse. Hence $\mathbf{P}^{-1}$ does not exist.

(See Subsection 4.2 for relevant material.)

## Solution to Activity 27

(a) $2\mathbf{A} - 3\mathbf{B} = 2 \begin{pmatrix} 1 & -2 \\ 4 & -6 \end{pmatrix} - 3 \begin{pmatrix} -2 & 3 \\ 1 & 0 \end{pmatrix}$

$= \begin{pmatrix} 2 & -4 \\ 8 & -12 \end{pmatrix} - \begin{pmatrix} -6 & 9 \\ 3 & 0 \end{pmatrix}$

$= \begin{pmatrix} 2 - (-6) & -4 - 9 \\ 8 - 3 & -12 - 0 \end{pmatrix}$

$= \begin{pmatrix} 8 & -13 \\ 5 & -12 \end{pmatrix}.$

(b) (i)   Taking out a scalar factor of $-5$ gives

$\mathbf{C} = \begin{pmatrix} -10 & -15 \\ 0 & -5 \end{pmatrix}$

$= -5 \begin{pmatrix} 2 & 3 \\ 0 & 1 \end{pmatrix}.$

(ii)  Taking out a scalar factor of $\frac{1}{2}$ gives

$\mathbf{D} = \begin{pmatrix} \frac{3}{2} & \frac{5}{2} \\ \frac{5}{2} & -\frac{1}{2} \end{pmatrix}$

$= \frac{1}{2} \begin{pmatrix} 3 & 5 \\ 5 & -1 \end{pmatrix}.$

## Solution to Activity 28

(a) $\mathbf{P}$ is a $3 \times 2$ matrix and $\mathbf{R}$ is a $2 \times 1$ matrix, so the product $\mathbf{PR}$ can be formed and its size will be $3 \times 1$.

$\mathbf{PR} = \begin{pmatrix} 2 & -3 \\ 4 & -1 \\ -2 & 1 \end{pmatrix} \begin{pmatrix} 2 \\ 1 \end{pmatrix}$

$= \begin{pmatrix} 2 \times 2 + (-3) \times 1 \\ 4 \times 2 + (-1) \times 1 \\ (-2) \times 2 + 1 \times 1 \end{pmatrix}$

$= \begin{pmatrix} 1 \\ 7 \\ -3 \end{pmatrix}.$

(b) $\mathbf{R}$ is a $2 \times 1$ matrix and $\mathbf{P}$ is a $3 \times 2$ matrix.

The number of columns of $\mathbf{R}$ is not equal to the number of rows of $\mathbf{P}$, so the product $\mathbf{RP}$ cannot be formed.

(c) $\mathbf{Q}^2 = \begin{pmatrix} -3 & 2 \\ 1 & 4 \end{pmatrix} \begin{pmatrix} -3 & 2 \\ 1 & 4 \end{pmatrix}$

$= \begin{pmatrix} (-3) \times (-3) + 2 \times 1 & (-3) \times 2 + 2 \times 4 \\ (1) \times (-3) + 4 \times 1 & 1 \times 2 + 4 \times 4 \end{pmatrix}$

$= \begin{pmatrix} 11 & 2 \\ 1 & 18 \end{pmatrix}.$

(d) Two matrices can be multiplied together only if the number of columns in the first matrix equals the number of rows in the second matrix. Hence a matrix can be multiplied by itself only if the number of columns is the same as the number of rows. Since $m \neq n$, it is not possible to calculate $\mathbf{M}^2$.

## Solution to Activity 29

(a)   $\mathbf{AI} = \begin{pmatrix} a_{11} & a_{12} \\ a_{21} & a_{22} \end{pmatrix} \begin{pmatrix} 1 & 0 \\ 0 & 1 \end{pmatrix}$

$= \begin{pmatrix} a_{11} \times 1 + a_{12} \times 0 & a_{11} \times 0 + a_{12} \times 1 \\ a_{21} \times 1 + a_{22} \times 0 & a_{21} \times 0 + a_{22} \times 1 \end{pmatrix}$

$= \begin{pmatrix} a_{11} & a_{12} \\ a_{21} & a_{22} \end{pmatrix}.$

and
$$\mathbf{IA} = \begin{pmatrix} 1 & 0 \\ 0 & 1 \end{pmatrix} \begin{pmatrix} a_{11} & a_{12} \\ a_{21} & a_{22} \end{pmatrix}$$
$$= \begin{pmatrix} 1 \times a_{11} + 0 \times a_{21} & 1 \times a_{12} + 0 \times a_{22} \\ 0 \times a_{11} + 1 \times a_{21} & 0 \times a_{12} + 1 \times a_{22} \end{pmatrix}$$
$$= \begin{pmatrix} a_{11} & a_{12} \\ a_{21} & a_{22} \end{pmatrix}.$$

Hence $\mathbf{AI} = \mathbf{IA} = \mathbf{A}$.

(b)  $\mathbf{BI} = \begin{pmatrix} b_{11} & b_{12} \end{pmatrix} \begin{pmatrix} 1 & 0 \\ 0 & 1 \end{pmatrix}$

$\quad = \begin{pmatrix} b_{11} \times 1 + b_{12} \times 0 & b_{11} \times 0 + b_{12} \times 1 \end{pmatrix}$

$\quad = \begin{pmatrix} b_{11} & b_{12} \end{pmatrix} = \mathbf{B}.$

$\mathbf{I}$ is a $2 \times 2$ matrix and $\mathbf{B}$ is a $1 \times 2$ matrix. So, the number of columns of $\mathbf{I}$ does not equal the number of rows of $\mathbf{B}$ and hence $\mathbf{IB}$ does not exist.

## Solution to Activity 30

(a)  We have $\det \mathbf{A} = 3 \times 4 - (-2) \times 1 = 14 \neq 0$. Therefore $\mathbf{A}$ is invertible and
$$\mathbf{A}^{-1} = \tfrac{1}{14} \begin{pmatrix} 4 & -1 \\ 2 & 3 \end{pmatrix}.$$

(b)  Here, $\det \mathbf{B} = 3 \times 6 - 2 \times 9 = 0$. Therefore $\mathbf{B}$ is not invertible.

(c)  We have $\det \mathbf{C} = -\tfrac{1}{2} \times (-3) - 6 \times \tfrac{2}{3} = -\tfrac{5}{2} \neq 0$. Therefore $\mathbf{C}$ is invertible and
$$\mathbf{C}^{-1} = -\tfrac{2}{5} \begin{pmatrix} -3 & -\tfrac{2}{3} \\ -6 & -\tfrac{1}{2} \end{pmatrix} = \tfrac{2}{5} \begin{pmatrix} 3 & \tfrac{2}{3} \\ 6 & \tfrac{1}{2} \end{pmatrix}.$$

## Solution to Activity 31

(a)  (i)  $y = (2x - 1)\left(3x^2 - \dfrac{4}{x}\right)$

$\qquad = 6x^3 - 3x^2 - 8 + \dfrac{4}{x}$

$\qquad = 6x^3 - 3x^2 - 8 + 4x^{-1}.$

Using the sum rule and the constant multiple rule gives
$$\frac{dy}{dx} = 6 \times 3x^2 - 3 \times 2x - 0 + 4 \times (-1)x^{-2}$$
$$= 18x^2 - 6x - \frac{4}{x^2}.$$

(See Subsection 5.1 for relevant material.)

(ii)  The function $y = e^{\cos(2x)}$ is a composite function. Let $u = \cos(2x)$. Then $y = e^u$.

Hence $\dfrac{du}{dx} = -2\sin(2x)$ and $\dfrac{dy}{du} = e^u$.

By the chain rule
$$\frac{dy}{dx} = \frac{dy}{du}\frac{du}{dx}$$
$$= (e^u)(-2\sin(2x))$$
$$= -2e^{\cos(2x)}\sin(2x).$$

(See Subsection 5.2 for relevant material.)

(iii)  The function $h(x) = x^3(\cos(2x) + \sin(2x))$ is a product of the two functions $f(x) = x^3$ and $g(x) = \cos(2x) + \sin(2x)$.

Differentiating the two functions gives
$$f'(x) = 3x^2$$
and
$$g'(x) = -2\sin(2x) + 2\cos(2x).$$

Applying the product rule,
$$h'(x)$$
$$= f(x)g'(x) + g(x)f'(x)$$
$$= x^3(-2\sin(2x) + 2\cos(2x))$$
$$\quad + (\cos(2x) + \sin(2x))(3x^2)$$
$$= x^2((2x + 3)\cos(2x)$$
$$\quad + (3 - 2x)\sin(2x)).$$

(See Subsection 5.2 for relevant material.)

(iv)  The function $s(t) = \dfrac{t}{\ln t}$ is a quotient formed from the two functions $f(t) = t$ and $g(t) = \ln t$.

Differentiating these two functions gives
$$f'(t) = 1 \text{ and } g'(t) = 1/t.$$

Applying the quotient rule,
$$h'(t) = \frac{g(t)f'(t) - f(t)g'(t)}{(g(t))^2}$$
$$= \frac{\ln t \times 1 - t \times 1/t}{(\ln t)^2}$$
$$= \frac{\ln t - 1}{(\ln t)^2}.$$

(See Subsection 5.2 for relevant material.)

(b) Differentiating the function
$$f(x) = 3x^4 + 4x^3 - 12x^2 + 1$$
using the sum and constant multiple rules gives
$$f'(x) = 12x^3 + 12x^2 - 24x.$$
The stationary points occur when $f'(x) = 0$, that is, when
$$12x^3 + 12x^2 - 24x = 0$$
$$12x(x^2 + x - 2) = 0$$
$$12x(x - 1)(x + 2) = 0.$$
Hence the stationary points occur at $x = 0$, $x = 1$ and $x = -2$. Now
$$f(0) = 3 \times 0^4 + 4 \times 0^3 - 12 \times 0^2 + 1 = 1,$$
$$f(1) = 3 \times 1^4 + 4 \times 1^3 - 12 \times 1^2 + 1$$
$$= 3 + 4 - 12 + 1 = -4,$$
and
$$f(-2) = 3 \times (-2)^4 + 4 \times (-2)^3$$
$$- 12 \times (-2)^2 + 1$$
$$= 3 \times 16 + 4 \times (-8) - 12 \times 4 + 1$$
$$= 48 - 32 - 48 + 1 = -31.$$
The coordinates of the stationary points are therefore $(0, 1)$, $(1, -4)$ and $(-2, -31)$.

Differentiating $f'(x) = 12x^3 + 12x^2 - 24x$ gives
$$f''(x) = 36x^2 + 24x - 24 = 12(3x^2 + 2x - 2).$$
Now
$$f''(0) = 12 \times (3 \times 0^2 + 2 \times 0 - 2) = -24,$$
$$f''(1) = 12 \times (3 \times 1^2 + 2 \times 1 - 2) = 36,$$
and
$$f''(-2) = 12 \times (3 \times (-2)^2 + 2 \times (-2) - 2)$$
$$= 12 \times (12 - 4 - 2) = 72.$$
Hence by the second derivative test, there is a local maximum at $(0, 1)$ and local minimums at $(1, -4)$ and $(-2, -31)$.

(See Subsection 5.3 for relevant material.)

(c) The velocity of the particle is given by
$$v = \frac{ds}{dt} = 50 - 10t.$$
Hence $\dfrac{ds}{dt} = 0$ when $50 - 10t = 0$, that is, when $t = 5$.
Now
$$\frac{d^2s}{dt^2} = -10.$$

So, by the second derivative test, there is a local maximum when $t = 5$. The maximum displacement (in m) of the particle is therefore
$$50 \times 5 - 5 \times (5)^2 = 125.$$
(See Subsections 5.3 and 5.4 for relevant material.)

## Solution to Activity 32

(a) $f(x) = 2\sin x - 4\cos x + 5\tan x$, so using the sum rule and the constant multiple rule gives
$$f'(x) = 2\cos x + 4\sin x + 5\sec^2 x.$$

(b) Here
$$g(x) = 7x^2 + \frac{5}{x} - x(2x^2 - 3) + 6$$
$$= 7x^2 + 5x^{-1} - 2x^3 + 3x + 6,$$
so
$$g'(x) = 14x - 5x^{-2} - 2 \times 3x^2 + 3$$
$$= 14x - \frac{5}{x^2} - 6x^2 + 3.$$

(c) By the properties of logarithms, we have
$$y = \ln(5x) = \ln(5) + \ln(x),$$
so
$$\frac{dy}{dx} = \frac{1}{x}.$$

(d) The function is
$$p = \frac{(q^2 - 3)(q + 1)}{q^2}$$
$$= \frac{q^3 + q^2 - 3q - 3}{q^2}$$
$$= q + 1 - 3q^{-1} - 3q^{-2}.$$
So
$$\frac{dp}{dq} = 1 + 3q^{-2} + 6q^{-3} = 1 + \frac{3}{q^2} + \frac{6}{q^3}.$$

## Solution to Activity 33

(a) (i) The function is $k(x) = x\sin x$.
Let $f(x) = x$ and $g(x) = \sin x$. Then $f'(x) = 1$ and $g'(x) = \cos x$. Hence, by the product rule,
$$k'(x) = f(x)g'(x) + g(x)f'(x)$$
$$= x\cos x + 1 \times \sin x$$
$$= x\cos x + \sin x.$$

(ii) The function is $y = e^x \tan x$.

Let $u(x) = e^x$ and $v(x) = \tan x$. Then $\dfrac{du}{dx} = e^x$ and $\dfrac{dv}{dx} = \sec^2 x$. Hence, by the product rule,

$$\begin{aligned}\frac{dy}{dx} &= u\frac{dv}{dx} + v\frac{du}{dx} \\ &= e^x(\sec^2 x) + (\tan x)(e^x) \\ &= e^x(\sec^2 x + \tan x).\end{aligned}$$

(iii) The function is $r = t^3 \ln t$.

Let $u(t) = t^3$ and $v(t) = \ln t$.

Then $\dfrac{du}{dt} = 3t^2$ and $\dfrac{dv}{dt} = \dfrac{1}{t}$.

Hence, by the product rule,

$$\begin{aligned}\frac{dr}{dt} &= u\frac{dv}{dt} + v\frac{du}{dt} \\ &= t^3\left(\frac{1}{t}\right) + (\ln t)(3t^2) \\ &= t^2(1 + 3\ln t).\end{aligned}$$

(b) We need to find the derivative of

$$p(t) = \sqrt{t}\sec t = t^{\frac{1}{2}}\sec t.$$

Let $f(t) = t^{\frac{1}{2}}$ and $g(t) = \sec t$. Then $f'(t) = \frac{1}{2}t^{-\frac{1}{2}}$ and $g'(t) = \sec t \tan t$.

Hence, by the product rule,

$$\begin{aligned}p'(t) &= f(t)g'(t) + g(t)f'(t) \\ &= (t^{\frac{1}{2}})(\sec t \tan t) + (\sec t)\left(\tfrac{1}{2}t^{-\frac{1}{2}}\right) \\ &= \sec t\left(t^{\frac{1}{2}}\tan t + \tfrac{1}{2}t^{-\frac{1}{2}}\right) \\ &= \frac{\sec t}{2\sqrt{t}}(2t\tan t + 1).\end{aligned}$$

The gradient at $t = \pi/3$ is therefore

$$p'\left(\frac{\pi}{3}\right) = \frac{\sec\left(\pi/3\right)}{2\sqrt{\pi/3}}\left(2\left(\frac{\pi}{3}\right)\tan\left(\frac{\pi}{3}\right) + 1\right)$$
$$= 4.522\ldots = 4.5 \text{ (to 1 d.p.)}.$$

**Solution to Activity 34**

(a) Since $k(x) = \dfrac{2x^3 + 1}{\ln x}$, we have $k(x) = \dfrac{f(x)}{g(x)}$ where $f(x) = 2x^3 + 1$ and $g(x) = \ln x$.

Now $f'(x) = 6x^2$ and $g'(x) = \dfrac{1}{x}$. Hence, by the quotient rule,

$$\begin{aligned}k'(x) &= \frac{g(x)f'(x) - f(x)g'(x)}{(g(x))^2} \\ &= \frac{(\ln x)(6x^2) - (2x^3 + 1)\left(\dfrac{1}{x}\right)}{(\ln x)^2} \\ &= \frac{6x^3\ln x - 2x^3 - 1}{x(\ln x)^2}.\end{aligned}$$

(b) As $r(y) = \dfrac{e^y - 1}{e^y + 1}$, we have $r(y) = \dfrac{f(y)}{g(y)}$ where $f(y) = e^y - 1$ and $g(y) = e^y + 1$.

Then $f'(y) = e^y$ and $g'(y) = e^y$. So, by the quotient rule,

$$\begin{aligned}r'(y) &= \frac{g(y)f'(y) - f(y)g'(y)}{(g(y))^2} \\ &= \frac{(e^y + 1)(e^y) - (e^y - 1)e^y}{(e^y + 1)^2} \\ &= \frac{2e^y}{(e^y + 1)^2}.\end{aligned}$$

(c) For

$$y = \frac{x^3}{x^2 + x + 1},$$

the top function is $x^3$ and the bottom function is $x^2 + x + 1$.

By the quotient rule,

$$\begin{aligned}\frac{dy}{dx} &= \frac{(x^2 + x + 1)(3x^2) - x^3(2x + 1)}{(x^2 + x + 1)^2} \\ &= \frac{3x^4 + 3x^3 + 3x^2 - 2x^4 - x^3}{(x^2 + x + 1)^2} \\ &= \frac{x^4 + 2x^3 + 3x^2}{(x^2 + x + 1)^2} \\ &= \frac{x^2(x^2 + 2x + 3)}{(x^2 + x + 1)^2}.\end{aligned}$$

(d) For
$$m(n) = \tan n = \frac{\sin n}{\cos n},$$
the top function is $\sin n$ and the bottom function is $\cos n$. By the quotient rule,
$$
\begin{aligned}
m'(n) &= \frac{(\cos n)(\cos n) - (\sin n)(-\sin n)}{\cos^2 n} \\
&= \frac{\cos^2 n + \sin^2 n}{\cos^2 n} \\
&= \frac{1}{\cos^2 n} = \sec^2 n.
\end{aligned}
$$

## Solution to Activity 35

(a) Since $y = e^{x^2}$, if we put $u = x^2$, then we have $y = e^u$.

This gives $\dfrac{du}{dx} = 2x$ and $\dfrac{dy}{du} = e^u$.

Hence, by the chain rule,
$$
\begin{aligned}
\frac{dy}{dx} &= \frac{dy}{du}\frac{du}{dx} \\
&= (e^u)(2x) = 2xe^{x^2}.
\end{aligned}
$$

(b) Here, $r = \sqrt{s^4 + 2s^2 + 3}$, so if we let $u = s^4 + 2s^2 + 3$, then $r = \sqrt{u}$.

This gives $\dfrac{du}{ds} = 4s^3 + 4s$ and $\dfrac{dr}{du} = \frac{1}{2}u^{-\frac{1}{2}}$.

So, by the chain rule,
$$
\begin{aligned}
\frac{dr}{ds} &= \frac{dr}{du}\frac{du}{ds} \\
&= \frac{1}{2}u^{-\frac{1}{2}}(4s^3 + 4s) \\
&= \frac{2(s^3 + s)}{\sqrt{s^4 + 2s^2 + 3}}.
\end{aligned}
$$

(c) We have $g(x) = \tan(cx)$, where $c$ is a constant.

Applying the chain rule directly gives
$$g'(x) = c\sec^2(cx).$$
Alternatively, let $y = g(x)$ and $u = cx$. Then $y = \tan u$.

This gives $\dfrac{du}{dx} = c$ and $\dfrac{dy}{du} = \sec^2 u$.

Hence, by the chain rule,
$$g'(x) = \frac{dy}{dx} = \frac{dy}{du}\frac{du}{dx} = (\sec^2 u) \times c = c\sec^2(cx).$$

(d) For $s(p) = \ln(p^4 + 1)$, applying the chain rule directly gives
$$s'(p) = \frac{1}{p^4 + 1} \times (4p^3) = \frac{4p^3}{p^4 + 1}.$$

Alternatively, if we let $y = s(p)$ and $u = p^4 + 1$, then $y = \ln u$.

This gives $\dfrac{du}{dp} = 4p^3$ and $\dfrac{dy}{du} = \frac{1}{u}$.

Hence, by the chain rule,
$$s'(p) = \frac{dy}{dp} = \frac{dy}{du}\frac{du}{dp} = \frac{1}{u}(4p^3) = \frac{4p^3}{p^4 + 1}.$$

## Solution to Activity 36

(a) For $z = \cos(2\theta)\sin(4\theta)$, using the product rule and then the chain rule gives
$$
\begin{aligned}
\frac{dz}{d\theta} &= \cos(2\theta)\frac{d}{d\theta}(\sin(4\theta)) + \sin(4\theta)\frac{d}{d\theta}(\cos(2\theta)) \\
&= 4\cos(2\theta)\cos(4\theta) - 2\sin(4\theta)\sin(2\theta) \\
&= 2(2\cos(2\theta)\cos(4\theta) - \sin(4\theta)\sin(2\theta)).
\end{aligned}
$$

(b) The function $f(x) = \dfrac{x\cos x}{x^2 + 4}$ has the form
$$f(x) = \frac{g(x)}{h(x)}, \text{ where } g(x) = x\cos x \text{ and}$$
$h(x) = x^2 + 4$. So we can use the quotient rule to differentiate $f(x)$, and we also need the product rule to differentiate $g(x)$.

Using the product rule gives
$$g'(x) = \cos x - x\sin x.$$
Also, $h'(x) = 2x$. Thus the quotient rule gives:
$$
\begin{aligned}
f'(x) &= \frac{(x^2 + 4)(\cos x - x\sin x) - (x\cos x)(2x)}{(x^2 + 4)^2} \\
&= \frac{(x^2 + 4 - 2x^2)\cos x - x(x^2 + 4)\sin x}{(x^2 + 4)^2} \\
&= \frac{(4 - x^2)\cos x - x(x^2 + 4)\sin x}{(x^2 + 4)^2}.
\end{aligned}
$$

## Solution to Activity 37

(a) $f(x) = x^4 - \frac{8}{3}x^3 + 2x^2 - 1$, so
$$
\begin{aligned}
f'(x) &= 4x^3 - 8x^2 + 4x \\
&= 4x(x^2 - 2x + 1) = 4x(x - 1)^2.
\end{aligned}
$$
Hence the equation $f'(x) = 0$ gives
$$4x(x - 1)^2 = 0,$$
which has solutions
$$x = 0 \quad \text{or} \quad x = 1 \text{ (twice)}.$$
The stationary points of $f$ are therefore 0 and 1.

(b) The nature of the stationary points can be determined by using the first derivative test.

Consider the values $-1$, $\frac{1}{2}$ and $2$. The values $-1$ and $\frac{1}{2}$ lie on each side of the stationary point $0$, and the values $\frac{1}{2}$ and $2$ lie on each side of the stationary point $1$.

The function $f$ is differentiable at all values of $x$ (as is every polynomial function).

Also, there are no stationary points between $-1$ and $0$, or between $0$ and $\frac{1}{2}$. Similarly, there are no stationary points between $\frac{1}{2}$ and $1$, or between $1$ and $2$.

Since $f'(x) = 4x(x-1)^2$, we have
$$f'(-1) = 4(-1) \times (-1-1)^2 = -16,$$
$$f'\left(\tfrac{1}{2}\right) = 4 \times \tfrac{1}{2} \times \left(\tfrac{1}{2}-1\right)^2 = \tfrac{1}{2},$$
$$f'(2) = 4 \times 2 \times (2-1)^2 = 8.$$

Hence the derivative is negative at $-1$ and positive at $\frac{1}{2}$, so the stationary point $0$ is a local minimum.

Similarly, the derivative is positive at $\frac{1}{2}$ and also positive at $2$, so the stationary point $1$ is a horizontal point of inflection.

(c) Since $f(0) = -1$ and
$$f(1) = 1^4 - \tfrac{8}{3} \times 1^3 + 2 \times 1^2 - 1 = -\tfrac{2}{3},$$
the coordinates of the stationary points are
$$(0, -1) \quad \text{and} \quad (1, -\tfrac{2}{3}).$$

(d) The graph of $f$ is shown below.

$$f(x) = x^4 - \tfrac{8}{3}x^3 + 2x^2 - 1$$

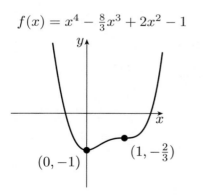

$(0, -1)$

$(1, -\tfrac{2}{3})$

**Solution to Activity 38**

(a) We have
$$f(x) = 3x^4 + \tfrac{1}{3}x^3 - \tfrac{1}{2}x^2 + 5,$$
so
$$\begin{aligned} f'(x) &= 12x^3 + x^2 - x \\ &= x(12x^2 + x - 1) \\ &= x(3x+1)(4x-1). \end{aligned}$$
Hence the stationary points of $f$ are $-\frac{1}{3}$, $0$ and $\frac{1}{4}$.

(b) We have
$$f''(x) = 36x^2 + 2x - 1,$$
so
$$f''\left(-\tfrac{1}{3}\right) = 36 \times \left(-\tfrac{1}{3}\right)^2 + 2\left(-\tfrac{1}{3}\right) - 1 = \tfrac{7}{3},$$
$$f''(0) = 36 \times 0^2 + 2 \times 0 - 1 = -1$$
and
$$f''\left(\tfrac{1}{4}\right) = 36 \times \left(\tfrac{1}{4}\right)^2 + 2\left(\tfrac{1}{4}\right) - 1 = \tfrac{7}{4}.$$
Hence, by the second derivative test, there is a local maximum at $x = 0$, and local minimums at $x = -\frac{1}{3}$ and $x = \frac{1}{4}$.

**Solution to Activity 39**

(a) The function is
$$f(x) = x^3 - 3x^2 - 10x + 20.$$
Hence
$$f'(x) = 3x^2 - 6x - 10$$
and
$$f''(x) = 6x - 6.$$
Solving $f''(x) = 0$ gives $x = 1$.

When $x < 1$, $f''(x) < 0$, and when $x > 1$, $f''(x) > 0$. Hence $f''(x)$ changes sign at $x = 1$, so there is a point of inflection at $x = 1$.

Notice that this is not a horizontal point of inflection, since $f'(1) \neq 0$.

(b) The function is
$$g(x) = x^4 - 8x^3 + 24x^2 - 32x + 40.$$
Hence $g'(x) = 4x^3 - 24x^2 + 48x - 32$ and
$$\begin{aligned} g''(x) &= 12x^2 - 48x + 48 \\ &= 12(x^2 - 4x + 4) \\ &= 12(x-2)^2. \end{aligned}$$

So $g''(x) = 0$ when $x = 2$.

When $x < 2$, $g''(x) > 0$, and when $x > 2$, $g''(x) > 0$. Hence $g''(x)$ does not change sign at $x = 2$. So there are no points of inflection in the graph of $g(x)$.

## Solution to Activity 40

(a) The height $s$ metres of the ball at time $t$ seconds is given by
$$s = 1.1 + 7t - 5t^2.$$
Hence the velocity $v\,\mathrm{ms}^{-1}$ of the ball at time $t$ seconds is given by
$$v = \frac{ds}{dt} = 7 - 10t,$$
and the acceleration $a\,\mathrm{ms}^{-2}$ of the ball at time $t$ seconds is given by
$$a = \frac{dv}{dt} = -10.$$

(b) When $t = 0.4$, we have
$$v = 7 - 10 \times 0.4 = 3,$$
and
$$a = -10.$$
So, the velocity is $3\,\mathrm{ms}^{-1}$ and the acceleration is $-10\,\mathrm{ms}^{-2}$.

(c) When $v = 0$,
$$7 - 10t = 0,$$
so $t = 0.7$. Hence the ball reaches its maximum height after 0.7 seconds.

(d) When $t = 0.7$,
$$s = 1.1 + 7 \times 0.7 - 5 \times (0.7)^2 = 3.55.$$
Hence the maximum height reached by the ball is 3.55 metres.

## Solution to Activity 41

(a) (i) $\int f(x)\,dx = \int (x-1)(2x+1)\,dx$
$$= \int (2x^2 - x - 1)\,dx$$
$$= \tfrac{2}{3}x^3 - \tfrac{1}{2}x^2 - x + c,$$
where $c$ is an arbitrary constant.

(ii) $\int g(t)\,dt = \int \dfrac{t^2 - 4}{t^3}\,dt$
$$= \int \left(\frac{1}{t} - \frac{4}{t^3}\right)\,dt$$
$$= \int \left(t^{-1} - 4t^{-3}\right)\,dt$$
$$= \ln|t| - 4 \times (-\tfrac{1}{2})t^{-2} + c$$
$$= \ln|t| + \frac{2}{t^2} + c,$$
where $c$ is an arbitrary constant.

(See Subsection 6.1 for relevant material.)

(b) The function $y = \sec(2x)$ is a composite function, so the chain rule can be used.

Let $u = 2x$ and $y = \sec u$. Then
$$\frac{du}{dx} = 2$$
and
$$\frac{dy}{du} = \sec u \tan u.$$
Hence, by the chain rule,
$$\frac{dy}{dx} = \frac{dy}{du}\frac{du}{dx}$$
$$= \sec u \tan u \times 2$$
$$= 2\sec(2x)\tan(2x).$$
Hence
$$\int \sec(2x)\tan(2x)\,dx$$
$$= \tfrac{1}{2} \int 2\sec(2x)\tan(2x)\,dx$$
$$= \tfrac{1}{2}\sec(2x) + c,$$
where $c$ is an arbitrary constant.

(See Subsection 6.1 for relevant material.)

(c) (i) $\dfrac{(2x-1)^2}{x^3} = \dfrac{4x^2 - 4x + 1}{x^3}$
$$= \frac{4}{x} - \frac{4}{x^2} + \frac{1}{x^3}$$
$$= 4x^{-1} - 4x^{-2} + x^{-3}.$$

Hence
$$\int_1^2 \frac{(2x-1)^2}{x^3}\, dx$$
$$= \int_1^2 (4x^{-1} - 4x^{-2} + x^{-3})\, dx$$
$$= \left[ 4\ln|x| + \frac{4}{x} - \frac{1}{2x^2} \right]_1^2$$
$$= \left( 4\ln 2 + \frac{4}{2} - \frac{1}{2 \times 2^2} \right)$$
$$\quad - \left( 4\ln 1 + \frac{4}{1} - \frac{1}{2 \times 1^2} \right)$$
$$= 4\ln 2 + 2 - \frac{1}{8} - 4 + \frac{1}{2}$$
$$= 4\ln 2 - \frac{13}{8}.$$

(ii) $\displaystyle\int_0^{\pi/4} (\cos 3\theta - \sin\theta)\, d\theta$

$$= \left[ \frac{1}{3}\sin 3\theta + \cos\theta \right]_0^{\pi/4}$$
$$= \left( \frac{1}{3}\sin\left(\frac{3\pi}{4}\right) + \cos\left(\frac{\pi}{4}\right) \right)$$
$$\quad - \left( \frac{1}{3}\sin 0 + \cos 0 \right)$$
$$= \frac{1}{3\sqrt{2}} + \frac{1}{\sqrt{2}} - 0 - 1$$
$$= \frac{4}{3\sqrt{2}} - 1.$$

(See Subsection 6.2 for relevant material.)

(d) The function $e^{4x}$ is positive on the interval $[-1, 1]$. So the area between the graph of $y = e^{4x}$ and the $x$-axis from $x = -1$ to $x = 1$ is given by

$$\int_{-1}^1 e^{4x}\, dx = \frac{1}{4}\left[ e^{4x} \right]_{-1}^1$$
$$= \frac{1}{4}(e^4 - e^{-4})$$
$$= 13.64\ldots = 13.6 \text{ (to 3 s.f.)}.$$

(See Subsection 6.2 for relevant material.)

(e) The interval formed by the limits of integration is $[-1, 1]$. However, the graph of $y = 1/x^2$ has a discontinuity at $x = 0$, which lies in this interval. Hence the fundamental theorem of calculus does not apply, and the integral cannot be evaluated.

(See Subsection 6.2 for relevant material.)

## Solution to Activity 42

(a) $\displaystyle\int 3x(x-1)^2\, dx = \int 3x(x^2 - 2x + 1)\, dx$

$$= 3\int (x^3 - 2x^2 + x)\, dx$$
$$= \frac{3}{4}x^4 - 2x^3 + \frac{3}{2}x^2 + c,$$

where $c$ is an arbitrary constant.

(b) $\displaystyle\int (\operatorname{cosec} x)(\operatorname{cosec} x + \cot x)\, dx$

$$= \int (\operatorname{cosec}^2 x + \operatorname{cosec} x \cot x)\, dx$$
$$= -\cot x - \operatorname{cosec} x + c,$$

where $c$ is an arbitrary constant.

## Solution to Activity 43

(a) The indefinite integral of $\sec^2 x$ is $\tan x + c$, so try differentiating $F(x) = \tan(ax)$.

By the chain rule, $F'(x) = (\sec^2(ax)) \times a$.

Hence,

$$\int \sec^2(ax)\, dx = \frac{1}{a}\int a\sec^2(ax)\, dx$$
$$= \frac{1}{a}\tan(ax) + c,$$

where $c$ is an arbitrary constant.

(b) If $y = \tan^{-1}\left(\dfrac{x}{a}\right)$, then by the chain rule,

$$\frac{dy}{dx} = \frac{1}{1 + (x/a)^2} \times \frac{1}{a}$$
$$= \frac{a}{a^2 + x^2}.$$

Hence

$$\int \frac{1}{a^2 + x^2}\, dx = \frac{1}{a}\int \frac{a}{a^2 + x^2}\, dx$$
$$= \frac{1}{a}\tan^{-1}\left(\frac{x}{a}\right) + c,$$

where $c$ is an arbitrary constant.

## Solution to Activity 44

(a) $\displaystyle\int_0^{\pi/4} 3\sin 4x \, dx$

$= \left[-\tfrac{3}{4}\cos(4x)\right]_0^{\pi/4}$

$= \left(-\tfrac{3}{4}\cos\left(4\times\left(\tfrac{\pi}{4}\right)\right)\right) - \left(-\tfrac{3}{4}\cos(4\times 0)\right)$

$= \tfrac{3}{4} + \tfrac{3}{4}$

$= \tfrac{3}{2}.$

(b) $\displaystyle\int_{-1}^0 e^t(1+e^{2t}) \, dt$

$= \displaystyle\int_{-1}^0 (e^t + e^{3t}) \, dt$

$= \left[e^t + \tfrac{1}{3}e^{3t}\right]_{-1}^0$

$= \left(e^0 + \tfrac{1}{3}e^{3\times 0}\right) - \left(e^{-1} + \tfrac{1}{3}e^{3\times(-1)}\right)$

$= \dfrac{4}{3} - \dfrac{1}{e} - \dfrac{1}{3e^3}.$

(c) $\displaystyle\int_1^e \frac{1}{2r} \, dr$

$= \tfrac{1}{2}\displaystyle\int_1^e \frac{1}{r} \, dr$

$= \left[\tfrac{1}{2}\ln|r|\right]_1^e$

$= \left(\tfrac{1}{2}\ln e\right) - \left(\tfrac{1}{2}\ln 1\right)$

$= \tfrac{1}{2}.$

## Solution to Activity 45

(a) The equation for $a$ in terms of $t$ is

$a = -9.8.$

Integrating this equation gives the following equation for $v$ in terms of $t$:

$v = -9.8t + c,$

where $c$ is a constant.

At the start of the motion, the velocity of the ball is $10\,\mathrm{m\,s^{-1}}$. That is, when $t = 0$, $v = 10$.

Substituting these values into the equation for $v$ above gives

$10 = -9.8 \times 0 + c, \quad$ that is, $\quad c = 10.$

So the equation for $v$ in terms of $t$ is

$v = 10 - 9.8t.$

(b) Integrating the equation found in part (a) gives the following equation for $s$ in terms of $t$:

$s = 10t - 9.8 \times \tfrac{1}{2}t^2 + c,$

that is,

$s = 10t - 4.9t^2 + c,$

where $c$ is a constant.

At the start of the motion, the displacement of the ball is $2\,\mathrm{m}$, because the ball is initially thrown from $2\,\mathrm{m}$ above the ground, and displacement is measured from ground level. Therefore, $s = 2$ when $t = 0$.

Substituting these values into the equation for $s$ above gives

$2 = 10 \times 0 - 4.9 \times 0^2 + c, \quad$ that is, $\quad c = 2.$

So the equation for $s$ in terms of $t$ is

$s = 10t - 4.9t^2 + 2.$

(c) When $t = 0.5$,

$v = 10 - 9.8 \times 0.5 = 10 - 4.9 = 5.1,$

and

$s = 10 \times 0.5 - 4.9 \times (0.5)^2 + 2$

$= 5 - 1.225 + 2 = 5.775.$

So the velocity of the ball half a second after it was thrown is $5.1\,\mathrm{m\,s^{-1}}$, and the displacement of the ball at the same time is approximately $5.8\,\mathrm{m}$ (to 2 s.f.), measured from the ground.

(d) When the ball has fallen back to the ground, the displacement is zero, that is, $s = 0$. Substituting this value of $s$ into the equation found in part (b) gives

$4.9t^2 - 10t - 2 = 0.$

The formula for solving a quadratic equation then gives the two solutions

$t = \dfrac{-(-10) \pm \sqrt{(-10)^2 - 4 \times 4.9 \times (-2)}}{2 \times 4.9}.$

Hence, $t = -0.18$ or $t = 2.2$ (both values to 2 s.f.).

The negative solution can be ignored, since $t \geq 0$. Hence the ball takes about 2.2 seconds to fall back to the ground.

# Acknowledgements

Grateful acknowledgement is made to the following sources:

Page 5: © Dave Bredeson / Dreamstime.com

Page 7: © Brian Chase / Dreamstime.com

Page 26: © Richard Gunion / Dreamstime.com

Page 38: © Emerka / Dreamstime.com

Page 39: © Jonshutt / Dreamstime.com

Page 53: © Jonshutt / Dreamstime.com

Page 62: © Foxyjoshi / Dreamstime.com

Every effort has been made to contact copyright holders. If any have been inadvertently overlooked the publishers will be pleased to make the necessary arrangements at the first opportunity.

# Mathematical typesetting

This is provided as a separate item.

Unit 3

# Number theory

# Introduction

Number theory is a branch of mathematics concerned with properties of the integers,

$$\ldots, -2, -1, 0, 1, 2, 3, \ldots .$$

The study of number theory goes back at least to the Ancient Greeks, who investigated the *prime numbers*,

$$2, 3, 5, 7, 11, 13, 17, \ldots ,$$

which are those integers greater than 1 with the property that each integer is divisible only by itself and 1.

The foundations of modern number theory were laid out by the eminent German mathematician Carl Friedrich Gauss, in his influential book *Disquisitiones Arithmeticae* (published in 1801). This text, which builds on the work of other number theorists such as Fermat, Euler, Lagrange and Legendre, was written when Gauss was only 21 years old!

Number theory continues to flourish today and it attracts popular attention through its many famous unsolved problems. Among these is *Goldbach's conjecture*, which asserts that every even integer greater than 2 can be written as the sum of two prime numbers. The German mathematician Christian Goldbach (1690–1764) made this conjecture in 1742, and yet it remains unproved today (although it has been verified by computer for all even integers up to $10^{14}$).

Carl Friedrich Gauss
(1777–1855)

Other famous conjectures in number theory have been proved in recent years, notably *Fermat's last theorem*, which says that it is impossible to find positive integers $a$, $b$ and $c$ that satisfy

$$a^n + b^n = c^n, \quad \text{where } n \text{ is an integer greater than 2.}$$

This assertion was made by the French lawyer and gifted amateur mathematician Pierre de Fermat. Fermat wrote in his copy of the classic Greek text *Arithmetica* that he had a truly wonderful proof of the assertion, but the margin was too narrow to contain it. After years of effort, with contributions by many mathematicians, the conjecture was finally proved in 1994, by the British mathematician Andrew Wiles (1953–). This proof is over 150 pages long and uses many new results so it seems highly unlikely that Fermat really did have a proof of his last theorem!

The early parts of Gauss's *Disquisitiones Arithmeticae* are about *congruences*, which are mathematical statements used to compare the remainders when two integers are each divided by another integer. Much of this unit is about congruences, and arithmetic involving congruences, which is known as *modular arithmetic*.

Pierre de Fermat (c. 1601–65)

Modular arithmetic is sometimes described as 'clock arithmetic' because it is similar to the arithmetic you perform on a 12-hour clock. For example, if it is 9 o'clock now then in 5 hours' time it will be 2 o'clock, as illustrated by the clocks in Figure 1 (in which the hour hands, but not the minute hands, are shown).

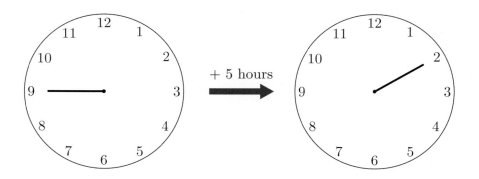

**Figure 1**  The left-hand clock shows 9 o'clock and the right-hand clock shows 5 hours later, 2 o'clock

The main goal of this unit is for you to become proficient at modular arithmetic, without the use of a calculator. In fact, you can put your calculator away, because you won't need it here at all.

There are many useful applications of modular arithmetic, and you'll see a selection of these later on. For instance, you'll learn about strategies using modular arithmetic for testing whether one integer is divisible by another. After reading about this, you'll be able to determine quickly whether the number

$$48\ 015\ 253\ 835\ 029$$

is divisible by 9.

You'll also find out how modular arithmetic is used to help prevent errors in identification numbers, such as the International Standard Book Number (ISBN) of a modern edition of *Disquisitiones Arithmeticae*, shown in Figure 2. The last digit of that ISBN, namely 6, is a 'check digit', which can be found from the other digits using modular arithmetic.

**Figure 2**  ISBN of *Disquisitiones Arithmeticae*

At the very end of the unit, you'll get a taste of how modular arithmetic is used to create secure means of disguising messages in the subject of *cryptography*. This subject is of particular importance in the modern era because of the large amount of sensitive data that is transferred electronically. You'll learn about a collection of processes for disguising information called *affine ciphers*, which, although relatively insecure, share many of the features of more complex processes in cryptography.

# 1 Euclid's algorithm and congruences

Central to this section is the observation that when you divide one integer by another, you are left with a remainder, which may be 0. You'll see how this observation is applied repeatedly in an important technique called *Euclid's algorithm*, which can be used to obtain the highest common factor of two integers. Towards the end of the section, you'll learn about an effective way of communicating properties of remainders using statements called *congruences*.

## 1.1  The division theorem

Let's begin by reminding ourselves of some terminology about numbers. The **integers** are the numbers

$$\ldots, -2, -1, 0, 1, 2, 3, \ldots,$$

and the **positive integers** or **natural numbers** are

$$1, 2, 3, \ldots.$$

It can be useful to represent the integers by equally spaced points on a straight line, as shown in Figure 3. This straight line is known as the **number line**. There are other points on the number line that don't correspond to integers, such as $1/2$, $\sqrt{3}$ or $\pi$, but in this unit we'll focus most of our attention on integers.

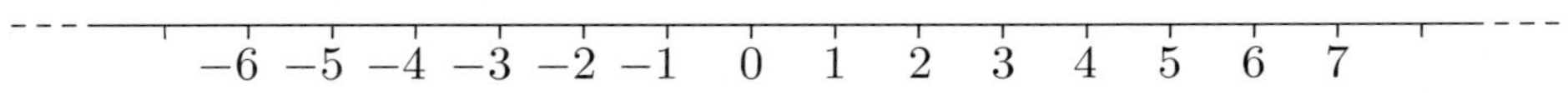

**Figure 3**   The integers on the number line

An integer $a$ is said to be **divisible** by a positive integer $n$ if there is a third integer $k$ such that $a = nk$. We also say that $a$ is a **multiple** of $n$, or $n$ is a **factor** or **divisor** of $a$. For example, 84 is a multiple of 12; also 84 is divisible by 12, and 12 is a factor or divisor of 84. In fact, $84 = 12 \times 7$. Sometimes mathematicians write $n|a$ to mean that $a$ is divisible by $n$, but that notation won't be used in this module.

Now consider the integers 38 and 5. Clearly, 38 is not a multiple of 5; in fact,

$$7 \times 5 < 38 < 8 \times 5,$$

or equivalently,

$$7 < \frac{38}{5} < 8.$$

We have 'trapped' 38/5 between two consecutive integers 7 and 8. The integer 7 on the left is known as the *quotient* on dividing 38 by 5.

Since $7 \times 5 = 35$, we see that 38 is 3 more than a multiple of 5. The number 3 is known as the *remainder* on dividing 38 by 5. You can write

$$38 = 7 \times 5 + 3.$$

quotient    remainder

This equation is represented on the number line in Figure 4.

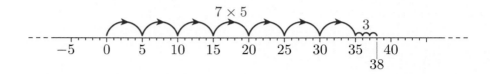

**Figure 4**    Dividing 38 by 5 on the number line

You obtain a quotient and remainder in this way whenever you divide one positive integer $a$ by another positive integer $n$. The remainder is 0 if $a$ is divisible by $n$, and otherwise it is a positive integer less than $n$.

Let's suppose now that $a$ is *negative*. For example, suppose you wish to divide $-38$ by 5. You can trap $-38/5$ between two consecutive integers as follows:

$$-8 < -\frac{38}{5} < -7.$$

Once again, the quotient is the integer on the *left*, namely $-8$. The remainder is then the difference between $-8 \times 5 = -40$ and $-38$, namely 2. You can write

$$-38 = (-8) \times 5 + 2.$$

quotient    remainder

This equation is represented on the number line in Figure 5.

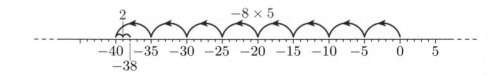

**Figure 5**    Dividing $-38$ by 5 on the number line

This time, the quotient is negative (the first eight jumps are to the left, rather than to the right), but it is chosen so that the remainder is still positive. The reason why we choose the quotient in this way to give a positive remainder is because this choice simplifies Euclid's algorithm, which you'll meet in the next subsection.

These observations about division can be summarised in **the division theorem**, sometimes known as **the division algorithm**, stated below. You can also find the division theorem and all the other important facts, definitions and techniques from this module in the MST125 *Handbook*.

**The division theorem**

Suppose that $a$ is an integer and $n$ is a positive integer. Then there are unique integers $q$ and $r$ such that

$$a = qn + r \quad \text{and} \quad 0 \leq r < n.$$

As you've learned already, the integer $q$ is called the **quotient** of the division, and $r$ is called the **remainder**. When $a = 29$ and $n = 7$, for example,

$$4 < \frac{29}{7} < 5,$$

so the quotient is 4. Or when $a = -29$ and $n = 7$, for example,

$$-5 < -\frac{29}{7} < -4,$$

so the quotient is $-5$. Once you've found the quotient, you can then find the remainder by rearranging $a = qn + r$ to give $r = a - qn$. The remainder satisfies $0 \leq r < n$, so, in particular, it is always positive or 0. It is 0 when $a$ is divisible by $n$.

**Example 1**   *Finding quotients and remainders*

For each of the following numbers $a$ and $n$, find the quotient $q$ and the remainder $r$ when you divide $a$ by $n$, and write down the equation $a = qn + r$.

(a) $a = 32$,   $n = 9$    (b) $a = -32$,   $n = 9$

**Solution**

(a) 🔍 Observe that $3 < 32/9 < 4$. The quotient is the left-hand value. 💭

$$q = 3,$$

🔍 Find the remainder using $r = a - qn$. 💭

$$r = 32 - 3 \times 9 = 5,$$

🔍 Write down the equation $a = qn + r$. 💭

and so

$$32 = 3 \times 9 + 5.$$

(b) 🔍 Observe that $-4 < -32/9 < -3$. The quotient is the left-hand value. 💭

$$q = -4,$$

🔍 Find the remainder using $r = a - qn$. 💭

$$r = -32 - (-4) \times 9 = 4,$$

🔍 Write down the equation $a = qn + r$. 💭

and so

$$-32 = -4 \times 9 + 4.$$

**Activity 1**   *Finding quotients and remainders*

For each of the following numbers $a$ and $n$, find the quotient and remainder when you divide $a$ by $n$, and write down the equation $a = qn + r$.

(a) $a = 59$,   $n = 7$    (b) $a = 84$,   $n = 12$    (c) $a = 100$,   $n = 9$

(d) $a = 9$,   $n = 100$    (e) $a = 0$,   $n = 11$    (f) $a = -58$,   $n = 5$

(g) $a = -100$,   $n = 9$    (h) $a = -96$,   $n = 12$    (i) $a = -4$,   $n = 5$

## 1.2   Euclid's algorithm

The **highest common factor** (HCF), or **greatest common divisor**, of two integers $a$ and $b$ is the greatest positive integer $n$ that is a divisor of both $a$ and $b$. For instance, the HCF of 18 and 30 is 6, because 6 is a divisor of both 18 and 30, and no integer greater than 6 is a divisor of both 18 and 30.

This subsection is about a procedure, known as Euclid's algorithm ('Euclid' is pronounced 'you-clid'), for finding the HCF of two integers. This important procedure is widely used in fields such as algebra, computer science and cryptography.

> **Euclid's Elements**
>
> Euclid was a Greek mathematician who worked in Alexandria around 300 BC. His most famous work was the influential textbook *Elements*, in which geometry is developed rigorously from a few foundational principles. *Elements* also contains some number theory, including observations about prime numbers and the procedure now known as Euclid's algorithm. The oldest complete text of *Elements* dates from the ninth century AD and is kept in the Bodleian library in Oxford.

A fragment of Euclid's *Elements*, dating from around 100 AD

An **algorithm** is a step-by-step procedure. One algorithm for finding the highest common factor of two integers involves finding the **prime factorisation** of each integer; that is, writing each integer as a product of prime numbers. Consider, for example, the two integers 252 and 120. Their prime factorisations are

$$252 = 2 \times 2 \times 3 \times 3 \times 7 \quad \text{and} \quad 120 = 2 \times 2 \times 2 \times 3 \times 5.$$

Now examine the prime factors of 252 and 120 one by one, and each time you find a factor that occurs in both factorisations place a circle round each of the matching factors, making sure that you ignore factors that are already circled. You obtain

$$252 = ②\times②\times③\times 3 \times 7 \quad \text{and} \quad 120 = ②\times②\times 2 \times③\times 5.$$

The product of the circled primes give the highest common factor, namely $2 \times 2 \times 3 = 12$. This method works well for small numbers like 252 and 120, but calculating prime factorisations of larger numbers can be a lengthy task. In fact, huge numbers with hundreds of digits often cannot be factorised into primes using even the most powerful computers in existence.

Euclid's algorithm is a much faster way of working out the highest common factor of two integers. In fact, if you apply the algorithm to the integers 252 and 120 then it produces the HCF so quickly that it's hard to get a good idea of how the method works! Here's a description of the algorithm for the pair of integers 207 and 60. The first step is to apply the division theorem to write down an expression of the form $207 = q \times 60 + r$. You find that

$$207 = 3 \times 60 + 27.$$

Ignore the quotient 3 for now, and instead focus on 60 (the smaller of our original pair of integers), and the remainder 27. Apply the division theorem to these two integers to obtain

$$60 = 2 \times 27 + 6.$$

Again, ignore the quotient 2, and apply the division theorem to 27 and 6 to obtain

$$27 = 4 \times 6 + 3.$$

Then apply the division theorem to 6 and 3 to obtain

$$6 = 2 \times 3 + 0.$$

Now stop, because you have obtained a remainder 0. In practice, you should list the equations one under another:

$$207 = 3 \times 60 + 27$$
$$60 = 2 \times 27 + 6$$
$$27 = 4 \times 6 + 3$$
$$6 = 2 \times 3 + 0.$$

With each step of Euclid's algorithm, the remainders decrease. This is because, for example, in the second step the remainder 6 is the remainder on dividing 60 by 27 and must therefore be less than 27 which is the remainder from the first step. It follows that there will eventually be a final step with remainder 0.

The remainder in the second-to-last step, which in this case is 3, is the highest common factor of our original integers 207 and 60 (as you'll see shortly).

You've now seen a description of how to apply Euclid's algorithm but haven't seen an explanation of why it works. In order to get a better understanding of why it works, first write down the pairs of integers used at each stage of the algorithm:

$$207, 60 \quad \longrightarrow \quad 60, 27 \quad \longrightarrow \quad 27, 6 \quad \longrightarrow \quad 6, 3.$$

The HCF of the pair $207, 60$ is the same as the HCF of the pair $60, 27$. To see why this is so, recall the first equation from Euclid's algorithm:

$$207 = 3 \times 60 + 27.$$

If 207 and 60 are both divisible by an integer $n$, then $3 \times 60$ is also divisible by $n$. This implies that $207 - 3 \times 60$ is divisible by $n$. So 27, which is equal to $207 - 3 \times 60$, is divisible by $n$ as well. Therefore any factor of both 207 and 60 is also a factor of both 60 and 27. Using the same kind of argument you can see that any factor of both 60 and 27 is also a factor of both 207 and 60. It follows that the HCF of 207 and 60 is equal to the HCF of 60 and 27.

With similar reasoning, you find that each pair of integers in the chain of arrows has the same HCF. The HCF of the final pair is 3, which is the remainder obtained in the second-to-last step of Euclid's algorithm. Therefore this remainder 3 is the HCF of 207 and 60.

**Strategy:**
**To find a highest common factor using Euclid's algorithm**

Suppose that $a$ and $b$ are positive integers.

1. By applying the division theorem repeatedly, form a list of equations:

$$a = q_1 b + r_1$$
$$b = q_2 r_1 + r_2$$
$$r_1 = q_3 r_2 + r_3$$
$$r_2 = q_4 r_3 + r_4$$
$$r_3 = q_5 r_4 + r_5$$
$$\vdots \qquad \vdots$$

2. Stop when you obtain an equation in which the remainder is 0.

3. The highest common factor of $a$ and $b$ is the remainder in the second-to-last equation.

**Example 2**   *Using Euclid's algorithm to find an HCF*

Find the highest common factor of 209 and 78.

**Solution**

🔍 Apply the division theorem repeatedly until a remainder of 0 is obtained. 💬

Euclid's algorithm gives

$$209 = 2 \times 78 + 53$$
$$78 = 1 \times 53 + 25$$
$$53 = 2 \times 25 + 3$$
$$25 = 8 \times 3 + 1$$
$$3 = 3 \times 1 + 0.$$

🔍 The highest common factor is the remainder found in the second-to-last equation. 💬

So the highest common factor of 209 and 78 is 1.

In this example, we could have omitted the last equation as we know that the remainders decrease at each stage. So, once we obtain a remainder of 1, we know that the remainder at the next stage must be 0 and so the highest common factor must be 1.

**Activity 2**   *Using Euclid's algorithm to find HCFs*

Using Euclid's algorithm, find the highest common factor of each of the following pairs of integers.

(a)  93 and 21      (b)  138 and 61      (c)  231 and 49

## 1.3  Bézout's identity

One of the many uses of Euclid's algorithm is to establish **Bézout's identity** ('Bézout' is pronounced 'beh-zoot').

> **Bézout's identity**
>
> Suppose that $a$ and $b$ are integers, not both 0, and let $d$ be their highest common factor. Then there are integers $v$ and $w$ such that
>
> $$av + bw = d.$$

For example, 2 is the highest common factor of 14 and 10, and

$$14 \times 3 + 10 \times (-4) = 2.$$

Like Euclid's algorithm, Bézout's identity is an extremely useful tool. You will need it later on when studying division in modular arithmetic.

Bézout's identity is named after the French mathematician Étienne Bézout. In fact, Bézout proved a more general result than the one given here, which was proved much earlier by another French mathematician, Claude Gaspard Bachet de Méziriac (1581–1638). Both Bachet's result and Bézout's more general result are usually referred to as Bézout's identity (or Bézout's lemma). As well as making important contributions to algebra, Bézout also wrote popular textbooks. Among these is the six-volume work *Cours complet de mathématiques*, published between 1770 and 1782. These books were used by students taking the entrance exams of the prestigious École Polytechnique in France, and they were also translated from French to English and employed by institutions such as Harvard University.

Étienne Bézout (1730–83)

Let's work out how to find the integers $v$ and $w$ in Bézout's identity for the pair of integers 207 and 60 considered earlier. The same method works whenever $a$ and $b$ are positive integers. Towards the end of this subsection you'll learn how to find $v$ and $w$ when $a$ and $b$ are not both positive.

We found that the HCF of 207 and 60 is 3, so we need $v$ and $w$ to satisfy

$$207v + 60w = 3.$$

First write down the steps of Euclid's algorithm again, omitting the final step, with remainder 0:

$$207 = 3 \times 60 + 27$$
$$60 = 2 \times 27 + 6$$
$$27 = 4 \times 6 + 3.$$

It is helpful to circle all the numbers apart from the quotients, like so:

$$\textcircled{207} = 3 \times \textcircled{60} + \textcircled{27}$$
$$\textcircled{60} = 2 \times \textcircled{27} + \textcircled{6}$$
$$\textcircled{27} = 4 \times \textcircled{6} + \textcircled{3}.$$

Now rearrange each of these three equations to make the remainders on the right the subjects of the equations:

$$\textcircled{27} = \textcircled{207} - 3 \times \textcircled{60}$$
$$\textcircled{6} = \textcircled{60} - 2 \times \textcircled{27}$$
$$\textcircled{3} = \textcircled{27} - 4 \times \textcircled{6}.$$

Next we use a process known as **backwards substitution**, in which we substitute into the bottom equation each of the expressions given on the right-hand side of this list of equations, working upwards one equation at a time. In doing this, we never combine the circled numbers with other numbers to simplify them: for example, we write $3 \times \textcircled{60}$ rather than 180, even though $3 \times 60 = 180$. The circles help you to remember not to simplify; think of a circled number as a variable.

Let's carry out backwards substitution. First substitute the expression for $\textcircled{6}$ from the second equation into the third equation:

$$\textcircled{3} = \textcircled{27} - 4 \times \left( \textcircled{60} - 2 \times \textcircled{27} \right).$$

This reduces to

$$\textcircled{3} = 9 \times \textcircled{27} - 4 \times \textcircled{60}.$$

Now substitute the expression for $\textcircled{27}$ from the first equation into this equation:

$$\textcircled{3} = 9 \times \left( \textcircled{207} - 3 \times \textcircled{60} \right) - 4 \times \textcircled{60}.$$

This reduces to

$$\textcircled{3} = 9 \times \textcircled{207} - 31 \times \textcircled{60}.$$

This equation is of the form described by Bézout's identity, namely,

$$207v + 60w = 3,$$

where $v = 9$ and $w = -31$.

(Check: $207 \times 9 + 60 \times (-31) = 1863 - 1860 = 3$.)

When calculating the integers $v$ and $w$ in Bézout's identity, you don't have to circle numbers as we have done here, although you may find that doing so avoids confusion.

Here's another example.

---

**Example 3**  *Finding integers $v$ and $w$ with $av + bw = d$ when $a$ and $b$ are both positive*

Find the highest common factor $d$ of 185 and 49, and then find integers $v$ and $w$ such that $185v + 49w = d$.

**Solution**

🔍 Apply Euclid's algorithm. 💬

Euclid's algorithm gives

$$185 = 3 \times 49 + 38$$
$$49 = 1 \times 38 + 11$$
$$38 = 3 \times 11 + 5$$
$$11 = 2 \times 5 + 1$$
$$5 = 5 \times 1 + 0.$$

🔍 The highest common factor is the remainder found in the second-to-last step. 💬

So the highest common factor of 185 and 49 is 1.

🔍 Rearrange all but the last equation to make the remainder the subject of each equation. 💬

Rearranging the equations gives

$$\boxed{38} = \boxed{185} - 3 \times \boxed{49}$$
$$\boxed{11} = \boxed{49} - 1 \times \boxed{38}$$
$$\boxed{5} = \boxed{38} - 3 \times \boxed{11}$$
$$\boxed{1} = \boxed{11} - 2 \times \boxed{5}.$$

🔍 Use backwards substitution to find integers $v$ and $w$ with $185v + 49w = 1$. First substitute the third equation into the fourth equation and simplify. 💬

Backwards substitution gives

$$\boxed{1} = \boxed{11} - 2 \times \left( \boxed{38} - 3 \times \boxed{11} \right)$$
$$= 7 \times \boxed{11} - 2 \times \boxed{38}.$$

💬 Substitute the second equation into this expression and simplify. 💬

$$= 7 \times \left( \circled{49} - 1 \times \circled{38} \right) - 2 \times \circled{38}$$
$$= 7 \times \circled{49} - 9 \times \circled{38}$$

💬 Substitute the first equation into this expression and simplify. 💬

$$= 7 \times \circled{49} - 9 \times \left( \circled{185} - 3 \times \circled{49} \right)$$
$$= 34 \times \circled{49} - 9 \times \circled{185}$$

So $185 \times (-9) + 49 \times 34 = 1$.

(Check: $185 \times (-9) + 49 \times 34 = -1665 + 1666 = 1$.)

Try the following activities, remembering to check your answers.

**Activity 3**    *Finding integers $v$ and $w$ with $av + bw = d$ when $a$ and $b$ are both positive*

(a) Find the highest common factor $d$ of 93 and 42, and then find integers $v$ and $w$ such that $93v + 42w = d$.

(b) Find the highest common factor $d$ of 70 and 29, and then find integers $v$ and $w$ such that $70v + 29w = d$.

So far in this subsection you've learned how to apply Euclid's algorithm and backwards substitution with *positive* integers $a$ and $b$ to obtain the equation $av + bw = d$ of Bézout's identity.

The next example shows you how to obtain the equation $av + bw = d$ when the integers $a$ and $b$ are not both positive.

**Example 4**   *Finding integers $v$ and $w$ with $av + bw = d$ when $a$ and $b$ are not both positive*

Find the highest common factor $d$ of 126 and $-33$, and then find integers $v$ and $w$ such that $126v - 33w = d$.

**Solution**

🔍 The HCF of 126 and $-33$ is the same as the HCF of the *positive* integers 126 and 33, which you can find using Euclid's algorithm. 💬

Euclid's algorithm gives

$$126 = 3 \times 33 + 27$$
$$33 = 1 \times 27 + 6$$
$$27 = 4 \times 6 + 3$$
$$6 = 2 \times 3 + 0.$$

So the HCF of 126 and 33 is 3, and hence the HCF of 126 and $-33$ is also 3.

🔍 To find integers $v$ and $w$ such that $126v - 33w = d$, you should begin by finding integers $v'$ and $w'$ such that $126v' + 33w' = d$ in the usual way. First rearrange all but the last equation above to make the remainder the subject of each equation. 💬

Rearranging the equations gives

$$\boxed{27} = \boxed{126} - 3 \times \boxed{33}$$
$$\boxed{6} = \boxed{33} - 1 \times \boxed{27}$$
$$\boxed{3} = \boxed{27} - 4 \times \boxed{6}.$$

🔍 Apply backwards substitution. 💬

Backwards substitution gives

$$\boxed{3} = \boxed{27} - 4 \times \left( \boxed{33} - 1 \times \boxed{27} \right)$$
$$= 5 \times \boxed{27} - 4 \times \boxed{33}$$
$$= 5 \times \left( \boxed{126} - 3 \times \boxed{33} \right) - 4 \times \boxed{33}$$
$$= 5 \times \boxed{126} - 19 \times \boxed{33}.$$

🔍 Rearrange the equation obtained above into the form $126v - 33w = d$. 💬

So

$$126 \times 5 - 33 \times 19 = 3.$$

This is the equation $126v - 33w = d$ with $v = 5$ and $w = 19$.

(Check: $126 \times 5 - 33 \times 19 = 630 - 627 = 3$.)

---

**Activity 4**   *Finding integers $v$ and $w$ with $av + bw = d$ when $a$ and $b$ are not both positive*

(a)  Find the highest common factor $d$ of $-112$ and $-91$, and then find integers $v$ and $w$ such that $-112v - 91w = d$.

(b)  Find the highest common factor $d$ of $-105$ and $39$, and then find integers $v$ and $w$ such that $-105v + 39w = d$.

Here's a puzzle that you might like to try to solve using Euclid's algorithm and backwards substitution.

**Activity 5**   *Using Euclid's algorithm and backwards substitution to solve a puzzle*

Suppose you have two buckets of capacities 23 litres and 16 litres, and a cauldron, which has capacity over 200 litres. You are able to fill the buckets with water from a tap. By using these buckets, you can obtain certain quantities of water in the cauldron. For example, you could obtain 7 litres of water in the cauldron by filling the 23-litre bucket from the tap and pouring it into the cauldron, and then filling the 16-litre bucket from the cauldron and emptying it out.

Is it possible to use a similar method to obtain exactly 1 litre of water in the cauldron? If so, describe how you would do this.

When working through many of the activities in this section, you'll have carried out several calculations. In the next activity you'll see how you can use the computer algebra system to carry out such calculations more quickly. This can be especially helpful when you're working with large numbers.

**Activity 6**   *Using the computer algebra system for number theory*

Work through Section 4 of the *Computer algebra guide*.

## 1.4 Congruences

In this subsection you'll learn about a useful way of comparing the remainders of two integers, called a *congruence*. Later on, congruences will be used in *modular arithmetic*. This type of arithmetic is central to number theory, and it also has applications in other disciplines, as you'll see.

Before discussing the full definition of a congruence, let's first look at a special case.

Two integers $a$ and $b$ are said to be **congruent modulo 5** if they each have the same remainder on division by 5. For example, 7 and 22 are congruent modulo 5 because each has remainder 2 on division by 5. The integers 7 and 22 are marked on the number line in Figure 6. You can see that they are congruent modulo 5 because they each lie two places to the right of a multiple of 5.

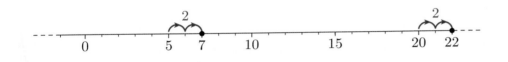

**Figure 6**   The integers 7 and 22 are congruent modulo 5

In contrast, the integers −12 and 6 are not congruent modulo 5 because −12 has remainder 3 on division by 5 whereas 6 has remainder 1 on division by 5. The integers −12 and 6 are marked on the number line in Figure 7. You can see that they are not congruent modulo 5 because −12 lies three places to the right of a multiple of 5 whereas 6 lies only one place to the right of a multiple of 5.

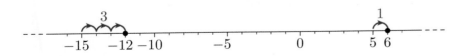

**Figure 7**   The integers −12 and 6 are not congruent modulo 5

The full definition of what it means to be congruent modulo $n$ is similar to the definition of what it means to be congruent modulo 5, but with a positive integer $n$ instead of 5.

> **Congruences**
>
> Let $n$ be a positive integer. Two integers $a$ and $b$ are **congruent modulo** $n$ if they each have the same remainder on division by $n$. If this is so then you write
>
> $$a \equiv b \pmod{n}.$$
>
> Such a statement is called a **congruence**.

For example, 19 and 12 are congruent modulo 7; that is,

$$19 \equiv 12 \pmod{7},$$

because 19 and 12 each have remainder 5 on division by 7. Also, $-8$ and 10 are congruent modulo 6; that is,

$$-8 \equiv 10 \pmod{6},$$

because $-8$ and 10 each have remainder 4 on division by 6. The integers $-8$ and 10 are marked on the number line shown in Figure 8. You can see that they are congruent modulo 6 because they each lie four places to the right of a multiple of 6.

**Figure 8**   The integers $-8$ and 10 are congruent modulo 6

It is important to remember when working with congruences that to find the remainder of a negative integer such as $-8$, on division by a positive integer $n$, you must find the multiple of $n$ immediately to the *left* of $-8$ on the number line, and from this multiple of $n$ count the number of places to the *right* you must move to get to $-8$. You'll get plenty of practice at finding remainders of negative integers in the rest of this unit.

**Activity 7**   *Checking congruences*

Which of the following congruences are true?

(a)  $11 \equiv 26 \pmod 5$       (b)  $9 \equiv -9 \pmod 5$

(c)  $28 \equiv 0 \pmod 7$       (d)  $-4 \equiv -18 \pmod 7$

(e)  $-8 \equiv 5 \pmod{13}$       (f)  $38 \equiv 0 \pmod{13}$

When working through this activity, you may have noticed that the congruence

$$a \equiv 0 \pmod n,$$

which says that $a$ has remainder 0 on division by $n$, is the same as the statement that $a$ is divisible by $n$. For example,

$$24 \equiv 0 \pmod 6$$

because 24 is divisible by 6.

> The word 'congruent' means 'in agreement'. The term makes its first appearance in modular arithmetic in Gauss's *Disquisitiones Arithmeticae*, which features in the introduction to this unit, although it was used much earlier than this by geometers. Gauss chose the symbol $\equiv$ because it is similar, but not identical, to the more familiar equals symbol $=$ . Congruences share many properties with, but are not identical to, equations.

For the next activity, which is about congruences modulo 10, remember that the **digits** of an integer are the numbers $0, 1, 2, \ldots, 9$ that make up that integer. The digits of 7238, for example, are 7, 2, 3 and 8.

**Activity 8**   *Understanding congruences modulo 10*

(a) Suppose that $a$ and $b$ are *positive* integers. By comparing the final digits of $a$ and $b$, can you determine whether they are congruent modulo 10?

(b) Does the method suggested in (a) work if $a$ is a positive integer but $b$ is a negative integer?

In Activity 7, you checked whether two integers were congruent modulo $n$ by finding their remainders modulo $n$. There is an alternative method for checking congruences, which is usually easier to apply.

> **Alternative method for checking congruences**
>
> The following statements are equivalent:
>
> - $a$ and $b$ are congruent modulo $n$
> - $a - b$ is divisible by $n$.
>
> So to check whether two integers $a$ and $b$ are congruent modulo $n$ you can check the second of these statements rather than the first.

For example, according to this alternative method, 27 and 12 are congruent modulo 5 because $27 - 12 = 15$, which is divisible by 5. In contrast, 9 and $-4$ are not congruent modulo 7 because $9 - (-4) = 13$, which is not divisible by 7. In fact, 27 and 12 both have remainder 2 on division by 5 so they are indeed congruent modulo 5. Also, 9 has remainder 2 and $-4$ has remainder 3 on division by 7, so it is true that 9 and $-4$ are not congruent modulo 7.

To understand why this alternative method works, you may find it is helpful to think of a number line.

If two integers $a$ and $b$ are congruent modulo $n$, then they have the same remainder modulo $n$. So the distance between $a$ and $b$ on the number line is an integer multiple of $n$. This distance is equal to $a - b$ when $a \geq b$, and to $b - a = -(a - b)$ when $b > a$. In either case, it follows that $a - b$ is divisible by $n$.

Similarly, if $a$ and $b$ are *not* congruent modulo $n$, then the distance between $a$ and $b$ is not an integer multiple of $n$; that is, $a - b$ is *not* divisible by $n$.

You can practise using the alternative method in the next activity. It will help you to remember that you can either test whether $a - b$ is divisible by $n$, or test whether $b - a$ is divisible by $n$, because the two tests are equivalent.

**Activity 9**    *Checking congruences using the alternative method*

Which of the following congruences are true and which are false?

(a) $63 \equiv 14 \pmod{7}$       (b) $-39 \equiv 39 \pmod{7}$

(c) $63 \equiv 14 \pmod{12}$      (d) $-8 \equiv 16 \pmod{12}$

(e) $-30 \equiv -17 \pmod{13}$       (f) $43 \equiv -87 \pmod{13}$

Another way of stating that $a - b$ is divisible by $n$ is to state that there is an integer $k$ (which may be negative) such that

$$a - b = kn;$$

that is,

$$a = b + kn.$$

This useful observation allows you to replace a congruence by an equation.

> **Writing a congruence as an equation**
>
> The congruence $a \equiv b \pmod{n}$ is equivalent to the statement that there is an integer $k$ such that
>
> $$a = b + nk.$$

For example, the congruence $7 \equiv 22 \pmod{5}$ is equivalent to the statement that there is an integer $k$ such that

$$7 = 22 + 5k.$$

There certainly is such an integer $k$, namely $k = -3$.

You should use this technique to approach the next activity.

> **Activity 10**  *Understanding congruences modulo 2*
>
> Explain why every odd number is congruent to 1 modulo 2. Explain why every even number is congruent to 0 modulo 2.

Let's finish this subsection with three basic properties of congruences, some of which you may have assumed to hold already. You might have realised, for example, that it is equivalent to write

$$3 \equiv 7 \pmod{4} \quad \text{or} \quad 7 \equiv 3 \pmod{4}.$$

This follows from the second property in the next box.

> **Properties of congruences**
> - $a \equiv a \pmod{n}$
> - if $a \equiv b \pmod{n}$ then $b \equiv a \pmod{n}$
> - if $a \equiv b \pmod{n}$ and $b \equiv c \pmod{n}$, then $a \equiv c \pmod{n}$

The first property just says that $a$ has the same remainder as itself on division by $n$. The second property is true because both congruences say that $a$ and $b$ have the same remainder on division by $n$. The final property says that if $a$ and $b$ have the same remainder on division by $n$, and $b$ and $c$ have the same remainder on division by $n$, then this is also true of $a$ and $c$.

The three properties are known, in order, as **reflexivity**, **symmetry** and **transitivity** of congruences. You won't need these terms in this module, but they are important mathematical concepts which you may meet again in the future.

You'll find that you use these properties of congruences without explicitly thinking about them. The third property shows, for example, that instead of writing

$$9 \equiv 2 \ (\text{mod } 7) \quad \text{and} \quad 2 \equiv -5 \ (\text{mod } 7),$$

it makes sense to write

$$9 \equiv 2 \equiv -5 \ (\text{mod } 7).$$

You can join several congruences together in this way, and only include (mod $n$) at the very end.

---

**Activity 11**   *Checking congruences involving several integers*

Which of the following statements are true and which are false? (All of the congruences in a statement must be true in order for the whole statement to be true.)

(a) $-7 \equiv 7 \equiv 17 \ (\text{mod } 10)$     (b) $-17 \equiv 3 \equiv 31 \equiv 67 \ (\text{mod } 2)$

(c) $-84 \equiv 0 \equiv 108 \ (\text{mod } 12)$

---

## 1.5   Residue classes

You have already seen that many integers have the same remainder on division by a positive integer $n$. For example, you saw that all the odd numbers are congruent to 1 modulo 2 and all the even numbers are congruent to 0 modulo 2. The odd integers are sometimes described as the *residue class* of 1 modulo 2. More generally, we have the following definition.

> **Residue class**
>
> Given any integer $a$, the collection of all integers congruent to $a$ modulo $n$ is known as the **residue class**, or **congruence class**, of $a$ modulo $n$.

The word 'residue' means 'remainder'. This term is used because the residue class of $a$ modulo $n$ is the class of those integers that have the same remainder on division by $n$ as $a$ does. For example, the residue class of 1 modulo 3 is shown on the number line in Figure 9.

**Figure 9**   The residue class of 1 modulo 3

Because 1, 4 and $-2$ are all congruent modulo 3, you could also describe the class of integers marked in Figure 9 as the residue class of 4 modulo 3, or as the residue class of $-2$ modulo 3.

Figure 10 shows the residue class of 0 modulo 3. These are the integers that are divisible by 3.

**Figure 10**   The residue class of 0 modulo 3

---

**Activity 12**   *Plotting residue classes on a number line*

(a)  Plot the residue class of 2 modulo 3 on a number line.

(b)  Plot the residue class of 1 modulo 4 on a number line.

(c)  Plot the residue class of $-1$ modulo 4 on a number line.

(d)  Plot the residue class of 0 modulo 5 on a number line.

---

You learned earlier (when you met the division theorem) that when you divide an integer $a$ by a positive integer $n$, the remainder $r$ satisfies

$$0 \leq r < n,$$

that is, $r$ is one of the numbers $0, 1, \ldots, n - 1$. Since $a$ and $r$ each have the same remainder (namely $r$) when divided by $n$, it follows that

$$a \equiv r \pmod{n}.$$

The remainder $r$ is also known as the *least residue* of $a$ modulo $n$, because it is the smallest number equal to or greater than 0 in the residue class of $a$ modulo $n$. In the next section you'll learn about modular arithmetic, and there you'll find that a calculation involving an integer $a$ can often be greatly simplified by performing the same calculation but using the least residue of $a$ modulo $n$ instead of $a$.

Least residues

The **least residue** of $a$ modulo $n$ is the remainder $r$ that you obtain when you divide $a$ by $n$.

The integer $r$ is one of the numbers $0, 1, \ldots, n-1$, and it satisfies

$a \equiv r \pmod{n}$.

---

**Example 5**  *Finding the least residue*

Find the least residue of $-33$ modulo 7.

**Solution**

🔍 Find the quotient and remainder when you divide $-33$ by 7. To do this, first notice that $-5 < -33/7 < -4$, so the quotient is $-5$. The remainder is then given by $a - qn$. 💬

Since $-33 = 7 \times (-5) + 2$, the least residue is 2.

---

**Activity 13**    *Finding least residues modulo 10*

Find the least residues of the following integers modulo 10.
(a) 17      (b) 50      (c) 6      (d) $-1$      (e) $-38$

**Activity 14**    *Finding least residues modulo 3*

Find the least residues of the following integers modulo 3.
(a) 17      (b) 9      (c) $-2$      (d) $-10$      (e) 3

Here's a puzzle that you might like to try to solve using residues.

**Activity 15**    *Finding the day of the week in 1000 days' time*

What day of the week will it be in 1000 days' time?

# 2 Modular arithmetic

**Modular arithmetic** is the application of the usual arithmetic operations – namely addition, subtraction, multiplication and division – for congruences. Addition, subtraction and multiplication are often simpler to carry out in modular arithmetic than they are normally, because you can use congruences to reduce large numbers to small numbers. For example, the multiplication $572 \times 863$ is difficult to calculate in your head, but working with congruences modulo 10 gives

$$572 \equiv 2 \pmod{10} \quad \text{and} \quad 863 \equiv 3 \pmod{10},$$

and you'll see later that this implies that

$$572 \times 863 \equiv 2 \times 3 \equiv 6 \pmod{10}.$$

You have to be more careful with division than the other arithmetic operations in modular arithmetic, so we leave division until the next section.

## 2.1 Addition and subtraction

Let's begin with two basic properties of congruences, which are useful for simplifying additions and subtractions.

**Addition and subtraction rules for congruences**

If $a \equiv b \pmod{n}$ and $c \equiv d \pmod{n}$, then

$$a + c \equiv b + d \pmod{n}$$
$$a - c \equiv b - d \pmod{n}.$$

To see why the first rule is true, remember that if $a \equiv b \pmod{n}$ and $c \equiv d \pmod{n}$, then both $a - b$ and $c - d$ are divisible by $n$. It follows that $(a - b) + (c - d)$ is divisible by $n$. But

$$(a - b) + (c - d) = (a + c) - (b + d),$$

so $(a + c) - (b + d)$ is divisible by $n$. Therefore $a + c \equiv b + d \pmod{n}$. A similar argument can be used to establish the second rule.

With practice, you'll soon get used to applying these rules, without the need to refer back to them. You'll find them helpful, for instance, in simplifying long additions with check digits later in this section. Let's look at some examples that highlight how the rules can be applied effectively. Suppose, for instance, that you are asked to find the least residue of $19 + 37$ modulo 18. One way to solve this is to first add 19 and 37 to get 56, and then find the least residue of 56 modulo 18, which is 2. There is an alternative method though: you can find the least residues of 19 and 37 modulo 18 *before* you add them.

You find that

$$19 \equiv 1 \ (\text{mod } 18) \quad \text{and} \quad 37 \equiv 1 \ (\text{mod } 18),$$

so, by the addition rule,

$$19 + 37 \equiv 1 + 1 \equiv 2 \ (\text{mod } 18).$$

It is important to remember that the *least* residue of the sum of two integers isn't necessarily equal to the sum of the least residues of those integers. For example, the least residue of $19 + 18$ modulo 10 is 7 (since $19 + 18 = 37$). On the other hand, the least residues of 19 and 18 modulo 10 are 9 and 8, respectively, so the sum of these residues is 17. You need to carry out one further step and note that the least residue of 17 modulo 10 is equal to 7 in order to obtain the least residue of the sum.

It is not always simpler to find least residues modulo $n$ before adding or subtracting. Suppose, for example, that you want to find the least residue of $85 - 84$ modulo 7. It is much easier to simply subtract 84 from 85 without first finding the least residues of each of these integers modulo 7. Sometimes there is scope for ingenuity in adding and subtracting in congruences, as the next example demonstrates.

---

**Example 6**  *Adding and subtracting in modular arithmetic*

Find the least residue of $171 + 169$ modulo 17.

**Solution**

🔍 You could first find the least residues of 171 and 169 modulo 17, but in this case it's easier to notice that both 171 and 169 are within 1 of 170, a multiple of 17, so they are congruent to 1 or $-1$ modulo 17. 💬

$$171 \equiv 1 \ (\text{mod } 17) \quad \text{and} \quad 169 \equiv -1 \ (\text{mod } 17)$$

🔍 Apply the addition rule for congruences. 💬

Therefore

$$171 + 169 \equiv 1 + (-1) \equiv 0 \ (\text{mod } 17).$$

So the least residue is 0.

---

You don't have to solve the problem in this way though. You could instead calculate $171 + 169 = 340$, and then observe that $340 \equiv 0 \ (\text{mod } 17)$.

In the following activities you should try to find each least residue using as simple a method as you can. Your methods may differ from those of the solutions provided, because there are many ways to carry out modular arithmetic. There's no need to use a calculator here; in fact, you'll develop a better understanding of modular arithmetic if you approach the activity without one.

**Activity 16**  *Adding and subtracting modulo 6*

Find the least residues of the following integers modulo 6.

(a) $7 + 3$     (b) $7 - 3$     (c) $23 - 24$

(d) $-3 - 19$     (e) $67 + 68$     (f) $601 - 6001$

**Activity 17**  *Adding and subtracting modulo 10*

Find the least residues of the following integers modulo 10.

(a) $6 + 4$     (b) $14 - 7$     (c) $13 - 15$

(d) $-21 - 17$     (e) $101 + 11 + 1$     (f) $101 - 11 - 1$

## 2.2  Multiplication and powers

Multiplication in modular arithmetic is simpler than multiplication in normal arithmetic because you can often replace the integers to be multiplied with simpler numbers before you multiply them. This is because of the following rule.

**Multiplication rule for congruences**

If $a \equiv b \pmod{n}$ and $c \equiv d \pmod{n}$, then

$$ac \equiv bd \pmod{n}.$$

To see why this rule is true, first note that if both $a - b$ and $c - d$ are divisible by $n$, then $(a - b)c + (c - d)b$ is also divisible by $n$. But

$$(a - b)c + (c - d)b = ac - bd,$$

so $ac - bd$ is divisible by $n$. Hence $ac \equiv bd \pmod{n}$.

You'll soon become familiar with the rules for addition, subtraction and multiplication, so you needn't commit them to memory. Let's consider an example. Suppose you wish to find the least residue of $52 \times 37$ modulo 7. It is difficult to work out $52 \times 37$ in your head. Instead, observe that

$$52 \equiv 3 \pmod{7} \quad \text{and} \quad 37 \equiv 2 \pmod{7},$$

so, using the multiplication rule,

$$52 \times 37 \equiv 3 \times 2 \equiv 6 \pmod{7}.$$

We simplified this multiplication by working with the least residues of 52 and 37 modulo 7. Sometimes it is better to choose an integer in a residue class other than the least residue, as the following example demonstrates.

**Example 7**    *Multiplying in modular arithmetic*

Find the least residue of $17 \times 14$ modulo 19.

**Solution**

🗨 Find integers small in absolute value that are congruent to 17 and 14 modulo 19. 🗨

$$17 \equiv -2 \ (\text{mod } 19) \quad \text{and} \quad 14 \equiv -5 \ (\text{mod } 19)$$

🗨 Apply the multiplication rule for congruences. 🗨

Therefore

$$17 \times 14 \equiv (-2) \times (-5) \equiv 10 \ (\text{mod } 19).$$

So the least residue is 10.

**Activity 18**    *Multiplying modulo 7*

Find the least residues of the following integers modulo 7.

(a) $3 \times 6$      (b) $22 \times 29$      (c) $(-5) \times 16$

(d) $51 \times 74$      (e) $47 \times (-25)$      (f) $(-29) \times (-44)$

**Activity 19**    *Multiplying modulo 8*

Find the least residues of the following integers modulo 8.

(a) $4 \times 4$      (b) $17 \times 26$      (c) $(-6) \times 34$

(d) $16 \times 457$      (e) $47 \times (-25)$      (f) $(-61) \times (-46)$

If $a \equiv b \ (\text{mod } n)$ then the multiplication rule for congruences gives

$$a^2 \equiv b^2 \ (\text{mod } n).$$

You can now apply the multiplication rule to

$$a \equiv b \ (\text{mod } n) \quad \text{and} \quad a^2 \equiv b^2 \ (\text{mod } n)$$

to give

$$a^3 \equiv b^3 \ (\text{mod } n).$$

Carrying on in this fashion, you obtain the power rule for congruences.

**Power rule for congruences**

If $a \equiv b \pmod{n}$, and $m$ is a positive integer, then
$$a^m \equiv b^m \pmod{n}.$$

For example, suppose you wish to find the least residue of $19^5$ modulo 9. Since $19 \equiv 1 \pmod 9$, it follows that
$$19^5 \equiv 1^5 \equiv 1 \pmod 9,$$
so the least residue is 1. This is a particularly simple application of the power rule. You'll usually need to do more working than this, as you'll see in the next example.

**Example 8**  *Raising to a power in modular arithmetic*

Find the least residue of $11^6$ modulo 9.

**Solution**

🗨 Use the power rule for congruences. 🗨

Since
$$11 \equiv 2 \pmod 9,$$
it follows that
$$11^6 \equiv 2^6 \pmod 9.$$

🗨 Start calculating powers of 2. 🗨

Calculating powers of 2 gives
$$2^2 = 4 \text{ and } 2^3 = 8.$$

🗨 You could continue in this way to obtain $2^6 = 64$, and then find the least residue of 64 modulo 9. There is a quicker method though. Since $8 \equiv -1 \pmod 9$, it follows that $2^3 \equiv -1 \pmod 9$. You can then jump straight to $2^6 = 2^3 \times 2^3$. 🗨

Since
$$2^3 \equiv -1 \pmod 9,$$
it follows that
$$2^6 = 2^3 \times 2^3 \equiv (-1) \times (-1) \equiv 1 \pmod 9.$$

So the least residue is 1.

Try the following activities. You may find that you use different methods to those given in the solutions.

---

**Activity 20**   *Raising to a power modulo 6*

Find the least residues of the following integers modulo 6.

(a)  $25^{25}$      (b)  $(-9)^4$      (c)  $20^6$

---

**Activity 21**   *Raising to a power modulo 13*

Find the least residues of the following integers modulo 13.

(a)  $25^{25}$      (b)  $54^4$      (c)  $16^9$

---

## 2.3  Fermat's little theorem

**Fermat's little theorem** is a fundamental result in number theory that helps you to calculate powers modulo $n$ when $n$ is a prime number. Not only is Fermat's little theorem central to number theory, it also has numerous applications in disciplines that require numeric computations; perhaps most significantly, it plays an essential role in *RSA ciphers*, which are widely used systems for disguising sensitive information. At the end of this unit, you'll learn about some other, similar, methods called *affine ciphers* that are used for disguising information.

> Fermat's little theorem was conceived by the French amateur mathematician Pierre de Fermat (referred to in the introduction) who in 1640 communicated the result in a letter to a friend along with the comment 'I'd send you the proof, but I fear that it is too long'. In fact, the earliest proof was published in 1736 by the Swiss mathematician Leonhard Euler (1707–83).

Before looking at Fermat's little theorem about powers modulo a general prime number, let's investigate the properties of powers modulo the prime number 5.

**Activity 22**   *Raising to the fourth power modulo 5*

Find the least residues of the following integers modulo 5.

(a) $1^4$    (b) $2^4$    (c) $3^4$    (d) $4^4$    (e) $7^4$

From parts (a) to (d) of this activity you should have found that

$$1^4 \equiv 2^4 \equiv 3^4 \equiv 4^4 \equiv 1 \pmod 5.$$

Suppose now that $a$ is any integer that is not a multiple of 5. We know that either

$$a \equiv 1 \pmod 5, \quad a \equiv 2 \pmod 5, \quad a \equiv 3 \pmod 5 \quad \text{or} \quad a \equiv 4 \pmod 5.$$

Therefore the power rule for congruences, together with the result of Activity 22, tells us that

$$a^4 \equiv 1 \pmod 5.$$

This observation about powers modulo 5 is a special case of Fermat's little theorem.

**Fermat's little theorem**

Let $p$ be a prime number, and let $a$ be an integer that is not a multiple of $p$. Then

$$a^{p-1} \equiv 1 \pmod p.$$

Since 5 is a prime number, Fermat's little theorem tells us immediately that all the least residues in Activity 22 are 1. Also, for example, 13 is a prime number, so

$$6^{12} \equiv 1 \pmod{13} \quad \text{and} \quad (-15)^{12} \equiv 1 \pmod{13}.$$

When applying Fermat's little theorem, remember that the integer $a$ must not be a multiple of $p$. After all, if $a$ is a multiple of $p$, then $a \equiv 0 \pmod p$, so $a^{p-1} \equiv 0 \pmod p$.

In some other texts the congruence $a^{p-1} \equiv 1 \pmod p$ in Fermat's little theorem is replaced with the alternative congruence

$$a^p \equiv a \pmod p.$$

You can obtain this congruence from $a^{p-1} \equiv 1 \pmod p$ by multiplying both sides by $a$. The theorem is less easy to apply in this alternative form but has the advantage that it is valid even if $a$ is a multiple of $p$. This is because, if $a$ is a multiple of $p$, then $a \equiv 0 \pmod p$, so

$$a^p \equiv a \equiv 0 \pmod p.$$

## Carmichael numbers and the Hardy–Ramanujan number

Fermat's little theorem tells us that if $n$ is a prime number, then

$$a^n \equiv a \ (\mathrm{mod}\ n)$$

for any integer $a$. This congruence may fail if $n$ is not a prime number; for example, if $n = 4$ and $a = 2$ then

$$2^4 \equiv 16 \equiv 0 \not\equiv 2 \ (\mathrm{mod}\ 4).$$

There are, however, some positive integers $n$ that are *not* prime numbers and yet have the property that the congruence $a^n \equiv a \ (\mathrm{mod}\ n)$ is true for every integer $a$. These positive integers are known as **Carmichael numbers** after the American mathematician Robert Daniel Carmichael (1879–1967) who discovered the smallest such number, namely 561.

The next two Carmichael numbers are 1105 and 1729, and there are infinitely many more of them. The integer 1729 is also known as the **Hardy–Ramanujan number** after a famous anecdote by the distinguished British mathematician Godfrey Harold Hardy (1877–1947) about a conversation he had with his friend Srinivasa Ramanujan. Ramanujan was an Indian mathematician of extraordinary talent who was ill in hospital at the time of the incident. Hardy gave the following account of their exchange on page 147 of an article titled 'The Indian Mathematician Ramanujan' which was published in 1937 in *The American Mathematical Monthly* (vol. 44, no. 3, pp. 137–55):

> I remember once going to see him when he was ill at Putney. I had ridden in taxi cab number 1729 and remarked that the number seemed to me rather a dull one, and that I hoped it was not an unfavorable omen. 'No,' he replied, 'it is a very interesting number; it is the smallest number expressible as the sum of two cubes in two different ways.'

In fact,

$$1729 = 1^3 + 12^3 = 9^3 + 10^3.$$

Srinivasa Ramanujan
(1887–1920)

Let's leave the justification of Fermat's little theorem for now – we'll return to it in a later unit – and instead consider an example of how the theorem can help us to calculate powers in modular arithmetic.

**Example 9**  *Applying Fermat's little theorem*

Find the least residue of $4^{20}$ modulo 7.

**Solution**

🔍 As 7 is a prime number, we can apply Fermat's little theorem. 💬

By Fermat's little theorem,

$$4^6 \equiv 1 \ (\text{mod } 7).$$

🔍 Therefore

$$4^{12} \equiv (4^6)^2 \equiv 1^2 \equiv 1 \ (\text{mod } 7),$$

$$4^{18} \equiv (4^6)^3 \equiv 1^3 \equiv 1 \ (\text{mod } 7),$$

and so forth; in fact, 4 to the power of *any* positive multiple of 6 is congruent to 1 modulo 7. In light of this, you can simplify the problem by writing 20 as a multiple of 6 plus a remainder term. 💬

Since

$$20 = 3 \times 6 + 2,$$

we obtain

🔍 Recall the usual index laws for calculating powers, which tell us that $4^{3\times6+2} = 4^{3\times6} \times 4^2 = (4^6)^3 \times 4^2$. 💬

$$4^{20} \equiv (4^6)^3 \times 4^2$$
$$\equiv 1^3 \times 4^2$$
$$\equiv 16$$
$$\equiv 2 \ (\text{mod } 7).$$

So the least residue is 2.

**Activity 23**  *Applying Fermat's little theorem with $p = 7$*

Find the least residues of the following integers modulo 7.

(a) $5^6$     (b) $18^{18}$     (c) $(-11)^{33}$

**Activity 24**  *Applying Fermat's little theorem with $p = 11$*

Find the least residues of the following integers modulo 11.

(a) $7^{10}$     (b) $(-5)^{31}$     (c) $13^{85}$

### Riffling

Riffling is a process for shuffling a deck of cards whereby you split the deck into two piles and then combine the two piles in such a way that the cards are interleaved. In a perfect riffle of a 52-card deck, the two piles each have 26 cards, and they are combined alternately, as shown below.

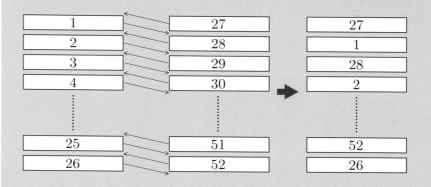

Just deal the cards, Fermat!

Have patience! Only twenty riffles to go!

The cards used here are numbered $1, 2, \ldots, 52$ according to their position in the original deck, with 1 the original top card and 52 the original bottom card. The deck is split into two piles, $1, 2, \ldots, 26$ and $27, 28, \ldots, 52$, as shown on the left in Figure 2.3. After the riffle, the card originally at position $x$ is moved to position $a$, where $a \equiv 2x \pmod{53}$. For example,

position 7 $\longrightarrow$ position 14,   and

position 27 $\longrightarrow$ position 1

because $27 \times 2 = 54$ and $54 \equiv 1 \pmod{53}$. It follows that after two consecutive perfect riffles, the card originally at position $x$ is moved to position $b$, where $b \equiv 2^2 x \pmod{53}$. Similarly, after 52 perfect riffles, the card originally at position $x$ is moved to position $c$, where $c \equiv 2^{52} x \pmod{53}$.

Fermat's little theorem tells us that

$2^{52} \equiv 1 \pmod{53}$,

which implies that $c \equiv x \pmod{53}$. That is, after 52 perfect riffles, the cards are returned to their original order!

## 2.4 Divisibility tests

Let's take a break from developing the properties of modular arithmetic, to look at how it is used in divisibility tests. A **divisibility test** is a method for checking whether one integer is divisible by another. For example, an integer is divisible by 2 if its last digit is $0, 2, 4, 6$ or $8$. Here you'll learn how modular arithmetic can be used to give a method for checking whether an integer is divisible by 3. This method can be adapted to give a test for divisibility by 9, as you'll see at the end of the subsection.

Let's start by looking at the test for divisibility by 3, then later on you'll see an explanation for how it works, using modular arithmetic. The **digit sum** of an integer is the number you obtain by adding together the digits of that number. For example, the digit sum of 5847 is 24, because

$$5 + 8 + 4 + 7 = 24.$$

If the integer is negative, then you should ignore the minus sign when working out the digit sum. For example, the digit sum of $-5847$ is also 24. The divisibility by 3 test is based on the following observation.

> **Divisibility by 3**
>
> If an integer is divisible by 3, then its digit sum is divisible by 3, and vice versa.

For instance, 6847 is not divisible by 3 because its digit sum 25 is not divisible by 3, whereas 5847 is divisible by 3 because its digit sum 24 is divisible by 3. With large numbers it may be difficult to tell whether the digit sum itself is divisible by 3, in which case you may need to find another digit sum, as shown in the next example.

**Example 10**  *Testing divisibility by 3*

Is the number 8 675 038 695 divisible by 3?

**Solution**

🔍 Find the digit sum of 8 675 038 695. 💬

The digit sum of 8 675 038 695 is

$$8 + 6 + 7 + 5 + 0 + 3 + 8 + 6 + 9 + 5 = 57$$

🔍 To determine whether 57 is divisible by 3, you can now find *its* digit sum. 💬

and the digit sum of 57 is

$$5 + 7 = 12.$$

Since 12 is divisible by 3, so is 57, and hence so is 8 675 038 695.

**Activity 25**  *Testing divisibility by 3*

Which of the following numbers are divisible by 3?

(a) 982      (b) 753      (c) 8364      (d) −9245

(e) 98 285 385 335      (f) $10^{100}$

Let's now see why the test for divisibility by 3 works. This explanation involves a four digit number; similar reasoning applies to a number with more (or fewer) digits. Any four digit number $n$ can be written as $10^3 a + 10^2 b + 10 c + d$, where $a$, $b$, $c$ and $d$ are the digits of the number.

For instance,

$$\underbrace{7263}_{n} = \underbrace{10^3 \times 7}_{10^3 a} + \underbrace{10^2 \times 2}_{10^2 b} + \underbrace{10 \times 6}_{10c} + \underbrace{3.}_{d}$$

Since

$$10 \equiv 1 \;(\mathrm{mod}\; 3),$$

it follows that, for any positive integer $n$,

$$10^n \equiv 1^n \equiv 1 \;(\mathrm{mod}\; 3).$$

Therefore

$$10^3 a + 10^2 b + 10 c + d \equiv a + b + c + d \;(\mathrm{mod}\; 3).$$

This shows that $n$ and its digit sum $a + b + c + d$ both have the same remainder on division by 3, so one is divisible by 3 as long as the other is divisible by 3.

This argument also works with congruences modulo 9 instead of modulo 3, and so there is a similar test for divisibility by 9.

**Divisibility by 9**

If an integer is divisible by 9, then its digit sum is divisible by 9, and vice versa.

For instance, 5847 is not divisible by 9 because its digit sum is 24 which is not divisible by 9, whereas 5841 is divisible by 9 because its digit sum is 18 which is divisible by 9.

**Activity 26** *Testing divisibility by 9*

Which of the following numbers are divisible by 9?

(a) 8469　　(b) 6172　　(c) 7 989 989 897 979 897

## Other divisibility tests

There are other tests that you can perform to test divisibility by numbers other than 3 and 9. Here are some of the simpler tests of this type.

To test whether an integer is divisible by 11, you should first find the *alternating digit sum* of the integer. The alternating digit sum is found by alternately adding and subtracting the digits of the integer, starting from the units digit, and working backwards through the other digits.

For example, the alternating digit sum of 673 148 is

$$8 - 4 + 1 - 3 + 7 - 6 = 3.$$

If the integer is divisible by 11, then its alternating digit sum is divisible by 11, and vice versa. Therefore 673 148 is not divisible by 11.

To test whether an integer is divisible by 4, you should first find the number formed from the final two digits of the original integer. For example, the final two digits of the integer 673 148 give the number 48. If the original integer is divisible by 4, then the number formed from the final two digits is divisible by 4, and vice versa. Therefore 673 148 is divisible by 4, as 48 is divisible by 4.

A similar divisibility test works for powers of 2 other than 4. For example, to test whether an integer is divisible by 8 (note that $8 = 2^3$), you just need to check whether the number formed from the final *three* digits of the integer is divisible by 8.

The correctness of these divisibility tests can be proved by using modular arithmetic.

## 2.5  Check digits

Groceries often have an identification number printed on them, accompanied by a barcode. The barcode is just a way of formatting the identification number so that it can easily be read by a scanner, and then identified from a database on a computer. Two barcodes are shown in Figure 11. On the left is an example of a Universal Product Code (UPC), which is a system of numbering used on many objects sold in the United Kingdom. On the right is an example of an International Standard Book Number (ISBN), which is a system of numbering used on books.

(a)                                            (b)

**Figure 11**    (a) A UPC (b) an ISBN

Sometimes errors may occur in communicating identification numbers; for example, a shop assistant may type an identification number incorrectly into a cash register. To help prevent such errors, the last digit is used as a check. It is known as a **check digit**. Here you'll learn how check digits work for ISBNs, using modular arithmetic. Check digits for other schemes work in a similar manner. Actually, you'll learn about 10-digit ISBNs, which were used before the introduction of 13-digit ISBNs in 2007. These 13-digit ISBNs also have check digits, but the explanation of how they work, although similar, is slightly more complicated.

Let's label the digits $a_1, a_2, \ldots, a_{10}$ of an ISBN in reverse order, so that $a_1$ is the check digit, as shown below for the ISBN of *Silent Spring*, by Rachel Carson.

| $a_{10}$ | $a_9$ | $a_8$ | $a_7$ | $a_6$ | $a_5$ | $a_4$ | $a_3$ | $a_2$ | $a_1$ |
|------|-----|-----|-----|-----|-----|-----|-----|-----|-----|
| 0 | 1 | 4 | 1 | 3 | 9 | 1 | 5 | 2 | ⑨ |

check
digit

The digits $a_2, a_3, \ldots, a_{10}$ identify the language, publisher and title of the book. The check digit $a_1$ is then defined to be the integer from $\{0, 1, 2, \ldots, 10\}$ that satisfies

$$a_1 \equiv -2a_2 - 3a_3 - 4a_4 - 5a_5 - 6a_6 - 7a_7 - 8a_8 - 9a_9 - 10a_{10} \pmod{11}.$$

Rearranging this congruence gives

$$a_1 + 2a_2 + 3a_3 + 4a_4 + 5a_5 + 6a_6 + 7a_7 + 8a_8 + 9a_9 + 10a_{10} \equiv 0 \pmod{11}.$$

An ISBN must satisfy this congruence in order to be valid. If the congruence is not satisfied, then there is an error and the number is not an ISBN. Let's check the ISBN of *Silent Spring*, using the symbol · as a shorthand for the multiplication symbol $\times$. The congruence check is satisfied because

$$a_1 + 2a_2 + 3a_3 + 4a_4 + 5a_5 + 6a_6 + 7a_7 + 8a_8 + 9a_9 + 10a_{10}$$
$$\equiv 9 + 2 \cdot 2 + 3 \cdot 5 + 4 \cdot 1 + 5 \cdot 9 + 6 \cdot 3 + 7 \cdot 1 + 8 \cdot 4 + 9 \cdot 1 + 10 \cdot 0$$
$$\equiv 9 + 4 + 15 + 4 + 45 + 18 + 7 + 32 + 9 + 0$$
$$\equiv 9 + 4 + 4 + 4 + 1 + 7 + 7 + 10 + 9$$
$$\equiv 55$$
$$\equiv 0 \pmod{11}.$$

The check digit $a_1$ is one of the integers $0, 1, 2, \ldots, 10$. When $a_1$ is 10, it is denoted in the ISBN by an X (the Roman numeral for 10) to ensure that it is represented by a single symbol.

The two most common types of errors when communicating ISBNs are interchanging two adjacent digits in the ISBN (for example, typing 123**54**6789X instead of 123**45**6789X) or altering a single digit (for example, typing **7**23456789X instead of **1**23456789X). The 10-digit code fails the ISBN congruence check if one of these errors occurs. To see why this is so, let's consider a valid ISBN with digits $a_1, a_2, \ldots, a_{10}$, in reverse order, which must satisfy the congruence check $S \equiv 0 \pmod{11}$, where

$$S = a_1 + 2a_2 + 3a_3 + 4a_4 + 5a_5 + 6a_6 + 7a_7 + 8a_8 + 9a_9 + 10a_{10}.$$

Suppose that in typing the ISBN you accidentally interchange $a_6$ and $a_7$ (but make no other errors). Your ISBN congruence check will now involve the sum

$$T = a_1 + 2a_2 + 3a_3 + 4a_4 + 5a_5 + \mathbf{6a_7} + \mathbf{7a_6} + 8a_8 + 9a_9 + 10a_{10}.$$

Unless $a_6 = a_7$ (in which case interchanging $a_6$ and $a_7$ won't matter) you obtain

$$T - S \equiv (6a_7 + 7a_6) - (6a_6 + 7a_7) \equiv a_6 - a_7 \not\equiv 0 \pmod{11}$$

(where $\not\equiv$ means 'is not congruent to'). Since $S \equiv 0 \pmod{11}$, it follows that $T \not\equiv 0 \pmod{11}$. Therefore your number fails the ISBN congruence check, so you know that you have made an error.

Next let's suppose instead that in typing the ISBN you accidentally change $a_{10}$ to a different digit $a'_{10}$ (but make no other errors). This time your congruence check will involve the sum

$$T = a_1 + 2a_2 + 3a_3 + 4a_4 + 5a_5 + 6a_6 + 7a_7 + 8a_8 + 9a_9 + \mathbf{10a'_{10}}.$$

Then

$$T - S \equiv 10a'_{10} - 10a_{10} \pmod{11}.$$

Remember that $10 \equiv -1 \pmod{11}$. Therefore

$$T - S \equiv (-1) \times a'_{10} - (-1) \times a_{10} \equiv a_{10} - a'_{10} \not\equiv 0 \pmod{11},$$

so again $T \not\equiv 0 \pmod{11}$. Since your number fails the ISBN congruence check, you know that you have made an error.

In this example of a single digit error we have assumed that $a_{10}$ is the incorrect digit. If the error was in a different digit, then the argument to show that

$$T - S \not\equiv 0 \ (\text{mod } 11)$$

is similar, but uses the idea of multiplicative inverses modulo 11, which you'll meet in the next section.

You've now seen that the congruence check will detect whether one of the two most common errors has occurred. However, it won't necessarily detect whether more than one of these errors has occurred, or if a different error has occurred.

---

**Example 11**  *Checking whether a 10-digit code could be an ISBN*

Does the following 10-digit code satisfy the ISBN congruence check?

0521683726

**Solution**

Label the digits $a_1, a_2, a_3, \ldots, a_{10}$ in reverse order, and evaluate $a_1 + 2a_2 + 3a_3 + 4a_4 + 5a_5 + 6a_6 + 7a_7 + 8a_8 + 9a_9 + 10a_{10}$

$$a_1 + 2a_2 + 3a_3 + 4a_4 + 5a_5 + 6a_6 + 7a_7 + 8a_8 + 9a_9 + 10a_{10}$$
$$\equiv 6 + 2 \cdot 2 + 3 \cdot 7 + 4 \cdot 3 + 5 \cdot 8 + 6 \cdot 6 + 7 \cdot 1 + 8 \cdot 2 + 9 \cdot 5 + 10 \cdot 0$$
$$\equiv 6 + 4 + 21 + 12 + 40 + 36 + 7 + 16 + 45 + 0$$

Simplify modulo 11.

$$\equiv 6 + 4 + 10 + 1 + 7 + 3 + 7 + 5 + 1$$
$$\equiv 44$$
$$\equiv 0 \ (\text{mod } 11)$$

So 0521683726 satisfies the ISBN congruence check.

---

You may find it helpful in carrying out the ISBN congruence check to remember that

$$10 \equiv -1 \ (\text{mod } 11), \quad 9 \equiv -2 \ (\text{mod } 11) \quad \text{and} \quad 8 \equiv -3 \ (\text{mod } 11).$$

**Activity 27**   *Checking whether 10-digit codes could be ISBNs*

Do the following 10-digit codes satisfy the ISBN congruence check?

(a)  0412606100      (b)  020142278X      (c)  0691118809

# 3  Multiplicative inverses and linear congruences

In this section you'll learn about *multiplicative inverses modulo n*, which give you a way of dividing in modular arithmetic. You'll use them to solve *linear congruences*; these are congruences such as

$$5x \equiv 2 \ (\mathrm{mod}\ 12),$$

where $x$ is an unknown.

In the subject of cryptography, linear congruences are used in procedures for disguising information called *ciphers*. At the end of the section you'll learn how to unravel particular types of ciphers, called *affine ciphers*, by solving linear congruences.

## 3.1  Multiplicative inverses

You've seen how to add, subtract and multiply in modular arithmetic, and now you'll learn how to divide in modular arithmetic. Let's begin with an example which demonstrates that you cannot divide both sides of a congruence by an integer in the way you might expect. Consider the congruence

$$20 \equiv 8 \ (\mathrm{mod}\ 6).$$

Even though 20 and 8 are each divisible by 4, with $20/4 = 5$ and $8/4 = 2$, you cannot divide both sides of the congruence by 4 because

$$5 \not\equiv 2 \ (\mathrm{mod}\ 6).$$

We need a different concept of division in modular arithmetic. To motivate this new concept, recall that in normal arithmetic, dividing by the integer 4, for example, is the same as multiplying by the reciprocal of 4, namely $\frac{1}{4}$. The reciprocal $\frac{1}{4}$ satisfies

$$4 \times \tfrac{1}{4} = 1.$$

In modular arithmetic, the only numbers used are integers, so we cannot multiply by the fraction $\frac{1}{4}$. Instead we need numbers that perform the same role as reciprocals, called *multiplicative inverses modulo n*.

> **Multiplicative inverses modulo $n$**
>
> A **multiplicative inverse of $a$ modulo $n$** is an integer $v$ such that
>
> $$av \equiv 1 \ (\mathrm{mod}\ n).$$

For example, 5 is a multiplicative inverse of 2 modulo 9 because

$$2 \times 5 \equiv 1 \ (\mathrm{mod}\ 9).$$

**Activity 28**  *Finding multiplicative inverses modulo 9*

Find a multiplicative inverse modulo 9 of each of the following integers.

(a) 1     (b) 5     (c) 7     (d) 16

For some integers $a$ and positive integers $n$, there is no multiplicative inverse of $a$ modulo $n$. For example, 3 doesn't have a multiplicative inverse modulo 9. To see this, suppose on the contrary that $v$ is a multiplicative inverse of 3 modulo 9. Then

$$3v \equiv 1 \ (\mathrm{mod}\ 9).$$

Let's now use the method explained near the end of Subsection 1.4 for writing a congruence as an equation. This method shows that our congruence is equivalent to the statement

$$3v = 1 + 9k,$$

for some integer $k$. However, the left-hand side of this equation is divisible by 3, but the right-hand side is not (because 3 is a factor of $9k$, so $1 + 9k$ is one more than a multiple of 3). This is impossible and so 3 doesn't have a multiplicative inverse modulo 9 after all.

**Activity 29**  *Showing that some integers don't have a multiplicative inverse modulo 9*

Show that each of the following integers doesn't have a multiplicative inverse modulo 9.

(a) 0     (b) 6     (c) 18

What's special about the integer 3 and each of the integers in Activity 29 is that they each share a common factor (other than 1) with 9. For instance, 3 and 9 share a common factor of 3. With reasoning similar to that used to solve Activity 29, you can show that any integer that shares a common factor (other than 1) with 9 doesn't have a multiplicative inverse modulo 9.

In contrast, the integer 2 and each of the integers from Activity 28 share no common factors with 9 other than 1. In other words, the highest common factor of any one of these integers and 9 is 1. Two integers whose highest common factor is 1 are said to be **coprime**. If $a$ and 9 are coprime integers, then $a$ *does* have a multiplicative inverse modulo 9. To see why this is so, remember that Bézout's identity tells us that if the highest common factor of $a$ and 9 is 1, then there are integers $v$ and $w$ such that

$$av + 9w = 1.$$

Therefore

$$av = 1 - 9w.$$

Using the method for writing a congruence as an equation, in reverse, we see that

$$av \equiv 1 \ (\text{mod } 9).$$

Therefore $v$ is a multiplicative inverse of $a$ modulo 9.

Arguing in a similar way but using modulo $n$ rather than modulo 9, you can obtain the following rule for deciding whether an integer $a$ has a multiplicative inverse modulo $n$.

**Existence of multiplicative inverses modulo $n$**

- If the integers $a$ and $n$ are coprime, then there is a multiplicative inverse of $a$ modulo $n$.

- If $a$ and $n$ are not coprime, then there is not a multiplicative inverse of $a$ modulo $n$.

You saw earlier that 5 is a multiplicative inverse of 2 modulo 9. It's not the only multiplicative inverse of 2 modulo 9 though; every integer that is congruent to 5 modulo 9 is a multiplicative inverse of 2 modulo 9. For example,

$$14 \equiv 5 \pmod 9, \quad \text{so} \quad 2 \times 14 \equiv 2 \times 5 \equiv 1 \pmod 9,$$
$$-4 \equiv 5 \pmod 9, \quad \text{so} \quad 2 \times (-4) \equiv 2 \times 5 \equiv 1 \pmod 9,$$

and so 14 and −4 are also multiplicative inverses of 2 modulo 9. Remember that the collection of integers congruent to 5 modulo 9 is called the residue class of 5 modulo 9. Among these integers is the least residue of 5 modulo 9, which is 5 itself. When you are asked to find a multiplicative inverse modulo $n$ it is usually clearest to give the least residue.

So far, you've found multiplicative inverses modulo $n$ by trying the values $1, 2, 3, \ldots, n - 1$ one by one. This method can, however, be very time consuming if $n$ is large! In the next example, you'll see how to find multiplicative inverses by using Euclid's algorithm and backwards substitution.

In general, you can use whichever method you wish, although a helpful rule to follow is that you should use the first method when $n \leq 13$, and otherwise use the second method. The reason for the integer 13 is that in modular arithmetic modulo $n$, where $n \leq 13$, the only pairs of integers that you'll need to multiply together are those that fall within the familiar 1 to 12 multiplication tables (providing that each of your integers is a least residue modulo $n$).

Sometimes you'll be able to find a multiplicative inverse with an intelligent guess, without using either of these methods. For example, to find the multiplicative inverse of 29 modulo 30, you just need to observe that

$$29 \equiv -1 \pmod{30},$$

so

$$29 \times 29 \equiv (-1) \times (-1) \equiv 1 \pmod{30}.$$

Therefore 29 is its own multiplicative inverse modulo 30.

**Example 12**    *Finding multiplicative inverses modulo $n$*

For each of the following values of $a$ and $n$, determine whether a multiplicative inverse of $a$ modulo $n$ exists and, if it does, find one.

(a)  $a = 5$, $n = 13$       (b)  $a = 30$, $n = 73$

**Solution**

(a)  To determine whether there is a multiplicative inverse, check whether 5 and 13 are coprime. They must be coprime, as they are both prime numbers.

The integers 5 and 13 are coprime, so there is a multiplicative inverse of 5 modulo 13.

Since $n \leq 13$, try the values $1, 2, 3, \ldots$ one by one until you find the multiplicative inverse modulo 13. You needn't necessarily check the integer 1, as clearly $5 \times 1 \not\equiv 1 \pmod{13}$.

$$5 \times 1 \equiv 5 \pmod{13} \qquad 5 \times 2 \equiv 10 \pmod{13}$$
$$5 \times 3 \equiv 15 \equiv 2 \pmod{13} \qquad 5 \times 4 \equiv 20 \equiv 7 \pmod{13}$$
$$5 \times 5 \equiv 25 \equiv 12 \pmod{13} \qquad 5 \times 6 \equiv 30 \equiv 4 \pmod{13}$$
$$5 \times 7 \equiv 35 \equiv 9 \pmod{13} \qquad 5 \times 8 \equiv 40 \equiv 1 \pmod{13}$$

Stop, as you have found an integer $v$ such that $5v \equiv 1 \pmod{13}$.

So 8 is a multiplicative inverse of 5 modulo 13.

You may have noticed a short cut that saves some calculations. You saw that $5 \times 5 \equiv 12 \equiv -1 \pmod{13}$, so $(-5) \times 5 \equiv -12 \equiv 1 \pmod{13}$. Since $-5 \equiv 8 \pmod{13}$, it follows that a multiplicative inverse of 5 modulo 13 is 8.

(b)  To determine whether there is a multiplicative inverse, check whether 30 and 73 are coprime. The numbers are quite large so use Euclid's algorithm to find the highest common factor.

Euclid's algorithm gives

$$73 = 2 \times 30 + 13$$
$$30 = 2 \times 13 + 4$$
$$13 = 3 \times 4 + 1$$
$$4 = 4 \times 1 + 0.$$

Since the second-to-last remainder is 1, the integers 30 and 73 are coprime, so there is a multiplicative inverse of 30 modulo 73.

Rearrange all but the last equation and then apply backwards substitution to find integers $v$ and $w$ with $30v + 73w = 1$. The integer $v$ will be a multiplicative inverse of 30 modulo 73 since $30v = 1 - 73w$.

Rearranging the equations gives

$$\boxed{13} = \boxed{73} - 2 \times \boxed{30}$$
$$\boxed{4} = \boxed{30} - 2 \times \boxed{13}$$
$$\boxed{1} = \boxed{13} - 3 \times \boxed{4}.$$

Backwards substitution gives

$$\boxed{1} = \boxed{13} - 3 \times \left( \boxed{30} - 2 \times \boxed{13} \right)$$
$$= 7 \times \boxed{13} - 3 \times \boxed{30}$$
$$= 7 \times \left( \boxed{73} - 2 \times \boxed{30} \right) - 3 \times \boxed{30}$$
$$= 7 \times \boxed{73} - 17 \times \boxed{30}.$$

(Check: $7 \times 73 - 17 \times 30 = 511 - 510 = 1$.)

Write the equation $7 \times 73 - 17 \times 30 = 1$ as a congruence modulo 73 to give the multiplicative inverse.

Since

$$(-17) \times 30 = 1 - 7 \times 73,$$

we obtain

$$(-17) \times 30 \equiv 1 \ (\text{mod } 73).$$

So $-17$ is a multiplicative inverse of 30 modulo 73.

The solution could end here, however, it is helpful to also find a multiplicative inverse that is a least residue modulo 73.

Since

$$-17 \equiv 56 \ (\text{mod } 73),$$

56 is also a multiplicative inverse of 30 modulo 73.

---

**Activity 30**   *Finding multiplicative inverses modulo $n$*

For each of the following values of $a$ and $n$, determine whether a multiplicative inverse of $a$ modulo $n$ exists and, if it does, find one.

(a)  $a = 10$, $n = 13$      (b)  $a = 12$, $n = 21$      (c)  $a = 18$, $n = 19$

(d)  $a = 0$, $n = 11$      (e)  $a = 7$, $n = 16$      (f)  $a = 10$, $n = 57$

(g)  $a = 84$, $n = 217$      (h)  $a = 43$, $n = 96$

## Basketball circles

Suppose 7 basketball players stand in a circle, equally spaced. One player has a ball and she throws it to the player 3 places to her right. The receiver then throws the ball 3 places to his right, and so forth. Let's label the people $0, 1, 2, \ldots, 6$ anticlockwise, starting with player 0 who begins with the ball. The path the ball follows is shown in Figure 12(a). After $m$ throws, the ball is with the player congruent to

$$\underbrace{3 + 3 + \cdots + 3}_{m \text{ copies of } 3} = 3m$$

modulo 7. For example, after 7 throws, player 0 has the ball again, because $3 \times 7 \equiv 0 \pmod 7$. After 5 throws, player 1 has the ball, because $3 \times 5 \equiv 1 \pmod 7$.

Now suppose there are $n$ basketball players (rather than 7) and each player throws the ball $a$ places (rather than 3) to his or her right. After $m$ throws, the ball is with the player congruent to $am$ modulo $n$. Therefore player 1 receives the ball when $m$ is a multiplicative inverse of $a$ modulo $n$. If $a$ and $n$ are *not* coprime, then player 1 never receives the ball, as is the case in Figure 12(b).

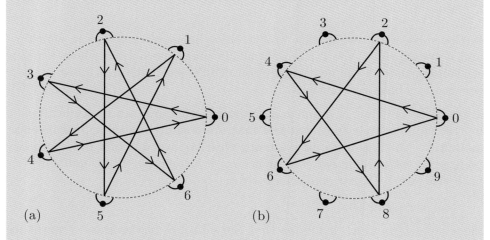

**Figure 12**   (a) A basketball circle with 7 players and throws of 3 places to the right (b) a basketball circle with 10 players and throws of 4 places to the right

## 3.2  Linear congruences

Congruences such as

$$5x \equiv 2 \ (\text{mod } 12),$$

in which there is an unknown $x$, are called *linear congruences*.

> **Linear congruences**
>
> A **linear congruence** is a congruence of the form
>
> $$ax \equiv b \ (\text{mod } n),$$
>
> where $a$ and $b$ are known, and $x$ is unknown.

The process of finding the values of $x$ for which a linear congruence is true is called **solving** the linear congruence. Any number $x$ for which the linear congruence is true is a *solution* of the linear congruence. If $x$ is a solution of a linear congruence, then any number in the same residue class as $x$ modulo $n$ is also a solution. So the solutions are given by linear congruences of the form

$$x \equiv c \ (\text{mod } n).$$

In this subsection, you'll learn how to solve linear congruences in which $a$ and $n$ are coprime. You'll learn about linear congruences in which $a$ and $n$ are *not* coprime in the next subsection. You'll see that some linear congruences have *no* solutions.

You saw earlier that, if $a$ and $n$ are coprime, then $a$ has a multiplicative inverse modulo $n$. In fact, you saw that $a$ has many multiplicative inverses modulo $n$. You'll now see how a multiplicative inverse $v$ of $a$ modulo $n$ can be used to solve the linear congruence $ax \equiv b \ (\text{mod } n)$. First, multiply both sides of the linear congruence by $v$:

$$vax \equiv vb \ (\text{mod } n).$$

Since $va \equiv 1 \ (\text{mod } n)$, it follows that the solutions of the linear congruence $ax \equiv b \ (\text{mod } n)$ are given by

$$x \equiv vb \ (\text{mod } n).$$

**Solving linear congruences when $a$ and $n$ are coprime**

If $a$ and $n$ are coprime, then the linear congruence $ax \equiv b \pmod{n}$ has solutions. The solutions are given by

$$x \equiv vb \pmod{n},$$

where $v$ is any multiplicative inverse of $a$ modulo $n$.

For example, consider the linear congruence

$$5x \equiv 6 \pmod{9}.$$

You saw earlier that 2 is a multiplicative inverse of 5 modulo 9 because

$$2 \times 5 \equiv 10 \equiv 1 \pmod{9}$$

and so the solutions of the linear congruence are given by

$$x \equiv 2 \times 6 \equiv 12 \equiv 3 \pmod{9};$$

that is,

$$x \equiv 3 \pmod{9}.$$

In other words, the solutions of the linear congruence consist of those integers congruent to 3 modulo 9 (such as $\ldots, -15, -6, 3, 12, 21, \ldots$). You can check this by substituting $x = 3$ back in to the original linear congruence:

$$5 \times 3 \equiv 15 \equiv 6 \pmod{9}.$$

In fact, for this particular linear congruence, it would be quicker simply to try out the values $1, 2, 3, \ldots$ one by one until you find a solution. We suggest that you apply this direct method for solving a linear congruence whenever $n \leq 13$. Let's consider some examples of linear congruences of this type, and return to linear congruences with $n > 13$ later on.

**Example 13**  *Solving a linear congruence when $a$ and $n$ are coprime and $n \leq 13$*

Solve the linear congruence

$$11x \equiv 7 \pmod 8.$$

**Solution**

🔍 Simplify the linear congruence by replacing 11 with the least residue of 11 modulo 8. 💬

Since $11 \equiv 3 \pmod 8$, an equivalent linear congruence is

$$3x \equiv 7 \pmod 8.$$

🔍 Check that this linear congruence has solutions. 💬

As 3 and 8 are coprime, this linear congruence has solutions.

🔍 Try the values $1, 2, 3, \ldots$ one by one until you find a solution. 💬

Trying the values $1, 2, 3, \ldots$ one by one, we find that

$$3 \times 1 \equiv 3 \pmod 8 \qquad 3 \times 2 \equiv 6 \pmod 8$$
$$3 \times 3 \equiv 9 \equiv 1 \pmod 8 \qquad 3 \times 4 \equiv 12 \equiv 4 \pmod 8$$
$$3 \times 5 \equiv 15 \equiv 7 \pmod 8.$$

So the solutions are given by

$$x \equiv 5 \pmod 8.$$

**Activity 31**  *Solving linear congruences when $a$ and $n$ are coprime and $n \leq 13$*

Solve the following linear congruences.

(a)  $2x \equiv 5 \pmod 7$     (b)  $7x \equiv 8 \pmod{10}$     (c)  $15x \equiv -13 \pmod{11}$

For large values of $n$, it is quicker to solve a linear congruence $ax \equiv b \pmod n$ by using the result you saw earlier. This states that the solutions are given by

$$x \equiv vb \pmod n,$$

where $v$ is a multiplicative inverse of $a$ modulo $n$.

**Example 14**   *Solving a linear congruence when $a$ and $n$ are coprime and $n > 13$*

Solve the linear congruence

$$7x \equiv 13 \pmod{24}.$$

**Solution**

🔍 Check that the linear congruence has solutions. 💬

As 7 and 24 are coprime, the linear congruence has solutions.

🔍 Since 24 is a large integer, use a multiplicative inverse of 7 modulo 24 to find the solutions. 💬

The solutions are given by

$$x \equiv 13v \pmod{24},$$

where $v$ is a multiplicative inverse of 7 modulo 24.

🔍 Use Euclid's algorithm and backwards substitution to find $v$. 💬

Euclid's algorithm gives

$$24 = 3 \times 7 + 3$$
$$7 = 2 \times 3 + 1.$$

🔍 There is no need to write down the next equation given by Euclid's algorithm since this equation has remainder 1. Apply backwards substitution to find integers $v$ and $w$ with $7v + 24w = 1$. There are only two equations, so you may choose not to rearrange them first. 💬

Backwards substitution gives

$$1 = 7 - 2 \times 3$$
$$= 7 - 2(24 - 3 \times 7)$$
$$= 7 \times 7 - 2 \times 24.$$

So

$$7 \times 7 \equiv 1 \pmod{24},$$

and hence 7 is a multiplicative inverse of 7 modulo 24. So the solutions are given by

$$x \equiv 13 \times 7 \equiv 91 \equiv 19 \pmod{24}.$$

🔍 Remember to check your answer. That is, check that if $x \equiv 19 \pmod{24}$ then $7x \equiv 13 \pmod{24}$. To do this, it helps to use the congruence $19 \equiv -5 \pmod{24}$. 💬

(Check: $7 \times 19 \equiv 7 \times (-5) \equiv -35 \equiv 13 \pmod{24}$.)

**Activity 32**    *Solving linear congruences when $a$ and $n$ are coprime and $n > 13$*

Solve the following linear congruences.

(a)  $7x \equiv 8 \pmod{20}$        (b)  $3x \equiv -26 \pmod{17}$

(c)  $13x \equiv 3 \pmod{30}$

Here's a puzzle that you might like to try to solve using linear congruences.

**Activity 33**    *Using linear congruences to solve a puzzle*

10 pirates discover a treasure chest containing no more than 100 gold coins. They share the coins out equally, but find there are 6 left over. In frustration they throw 3 of their comrades overboard, and share the coins out equally again among the remaining 7. This time the coins can be distributed equally, with none left over. How many coins are there?

Hint: let $N$ be the number of gold coins. When the 10 pirates first share the $N$ coins out, they find there are 6 left over. Write this observation as a congruence modulo 10. After 3 pirates are thrown overboard, the remaining 7 pirates succeed in sharing out the $N$ coins equally among themselves. Use this fact to write down an expression for $N$ that you can substitute into the congruence that you wrote down earlier to give you a linear congruence.

## 3.3  More linear congruences

In this subsection you'll learn about linear congruences $ax \equiv b \pmod{n}$ for which $a$ and $n$ are *not* coprime. This is a bit more complicated than the case when $a$ and $n$ *are* coprime.

Let's begin with an example, the linear congruence

$$6x \equiv 4 \pmod{15}.$$

This is unlike any of the linear congruences you met earlier because the integers $a$ and $n$ (6 and 15) are not coprime: their highest common factor is 3. If $x$ is a solution of this linear congruence, then you can write

$$6x = 4 + 15k,$$

for some integer $k$. Subtracting $15k$ from both sides gives

$$6x - 15k = 4.$$

However, the left-hand side of this equation is divisible by 3 but the right-hand side is not. This contradiction shows that there are *no* solutions of the linear congruence $6x \equiv 4 \pmod{15}$.

Similar arguments can be used to obtain the following more general result.

> ### Linear congruences without solutions
>
> Let $d$ be the highest common factor of the integers $a$ and $n$, where $n > 1$. The linear congruence
>
> $$ax \equiv b \ (\text{mod } n)$$
>
> has no solutions if $b$ is not divisible by $d$.

For example, the linear congruence

$$-15x \equiv 8 \ (\text{mod } 20)$$

has no solutions, because the highest common factor of $-15$ and $20$ is $5$, and $8$ is not divisible by $5$.

### Activity 34   *Showing that some linear congruences have no solutions*

Show that the following linear congruences have no solutions.

(a) $4x \equiv 5 \ (\text{mod } 10)$     (b) $-12x \equiv 8 \ (\text{mod } 42)$

(c) $48x \equiv 70 \ (\text{mod } 111)$

So far you've learned how to solve the linear congruence

$$ax \equiv b \ (\text{mod } n)$$

when $a$ and $n$ are coprime, and you've seen that the linear congruence has no solutions when $b$ is not divisible by the highest common factor of $a$ and $n$. Let's suppose now that the linear congruence doesn't fall into either of these categories: so the highest common factor of $a$ and $n$ is not 1, but it is a divisor of $b$. For example, consider the linear congruence

$$9x \equiv 21 \ (\text{mod } 24).$$

The highest common factor of 9 and 24 is 3, and 3 is a divisor of 21. The linear congruence is equivalent to the statement that

$$9x = 21 + 24k, \quad \text{for some integer } k.$$

If we divide each side of this equation by 3, the highest common factor of 9 and 24, then we obtain

$$3x = 7 + 8k, \quad \text{for some integer } k.$$

Expressed as a linear congruence, this statement says that

$$3x \equiv 7 \ (\text{mod } 8).$$

This new linear congruence is equivalent to the original one, $9x \equiv 21 \ (\text{mod } 24)$. However, the new linear congruence is of the form $ax \equiv b \ (\text{mod } n)$, where $a$ and $n$ *are* coprime, so you can solve it using the methods of the previous subsection. In fact, you saw how to solve it in Example 13; the solutions are given by

$$x \equiv 5 \ (\mathrm{mod} \ 8).$$

Notice that the original linear congruence was a congruence modulo 24 whereas the solutions are given by a congruence modulo 8.

This method works with other linear congruences of a similar type. It is summarised as follows.

---

**Linear congruences with solutions**

Let $d$ be the highest common factor of the integers $a$ and $n$, where $n > 1$. The linear congruence

$$ax \equiv b \ (\mathrm{mod} \ n)$$

has solutions if $b$ is divisible by $d$. The solutions are given by the solutions of the equivalent linear congruence

$$\frac{a}{d} x \equiv \frac{b}{d} \left( \mathrm{mod} \ \frac{n}{d} \right).$$

---

It's worth emphasising here that if $b$ is divisible by $d$ then the numbers $a/d$, $b/d$ and $n/d$ are all integers. (You should not write down a congruence involving a number that is not an integer.) What is more, after dividing $a$ and $n$ by their highest common factor $d$, you are left with integers $a/d$ and $n/d$ with no common factors (other than 1). That is, $a/d$ and $n/d$ are coprime, so you can solve the linear congruence

$$\frac{a}{d} x \equiv \frac{b}{d} \left( \mathrm{mod} \ \frac{n}{d} \right)$$

using the techniques of the previous subsection.

Notice that the statement in the box is true even if $d = 1$ (that is, even if $a$ and $n$ are coprime) although in that case it doesn't tell you anything useful because if $d = 1$ then the two linear congruences

$$ax \equiv b \ (\mathrm{mod} \ n) \quad \text{and} \quad \frac{a}{d} x \equiv \frac{b}{d} \left( \mathrm{mod} \ \frac{n}{d} \right)$$

are identical.

**Example 15**   *Solving a linear congruence when $a$ and $n$ are not coprime*

Solve the linear congruence $12x \equiv 16 \pmod{20}$.

**Solution**

🔍 Check that the linear congruence has solutions. 💬

The highest common factor of 12 and 20 is 4. Since 16 is divisible by 4, the linear congruence has solutions.

🔍 Divide each of the integers 12, 16 and 20 in the linear congruence $12x \equiv 16 \pmod{20}$ by 4 to obtain an equivalent linear congruence. 💬

and is equivalent to

$$3x \equiv 4 \pmod{5}.$$

🔍 Since the numbers involved are small, try the values $1, 2, 3, \ldots$ one by one until you find a solution. 💬

Trying the values $1, 2, 3, \ldots$ one by one, we find that

$$3 \times 1 \equiv 3 \pmod{5} \qquad 3 \times 2 \equiv 6 \equiv 1 \pmod{5}$$
$$3 \times 3 \equiv 9 \equiv 4 \pmod{5}.$$

So the solutions are given by

$$x \equiv 3 \pmod{5}.$$

**Activity 35**   *Solving linear congruences when $a$ and $n$ are not coprime*

Solve the following linear congruences.

(a)  $12x \equiv 6 \pmod{15}$      (b)  $-25x \equiv 10 \pmod{40}$

(c)  $18x \equiv 6 \pmod{98}$

You now know how to determine whether a linear congruence has solutions and, if so, how to find the solutions. The results that you've met are summarised as follows.

Solving the linear congruence $ax \equiv b \pmod{n}$

Let $d$ be the highest common factor of $a$ and $n$.

- If $d = 1$, then the linear congruence has solutions. The solutions are given by
$$x \equiv vb \pmod{n},$$
where $v$ is any multiplicative inverse of $a$ modulo $n$.

- If $b$ is not divisible by $d$, then the linear congruence has no solutions.

- If $b$ is divisible by $d$, then the linear congruence has solutions and the solutions are given by the solutions of the equivalent linear congruence
$$\frac{a}{d}x \equiv \frac{b}{d} \left( \bmod \ \frac{n}{d} \right).$$

You may also find the decision tree in Figure 13 helpful.

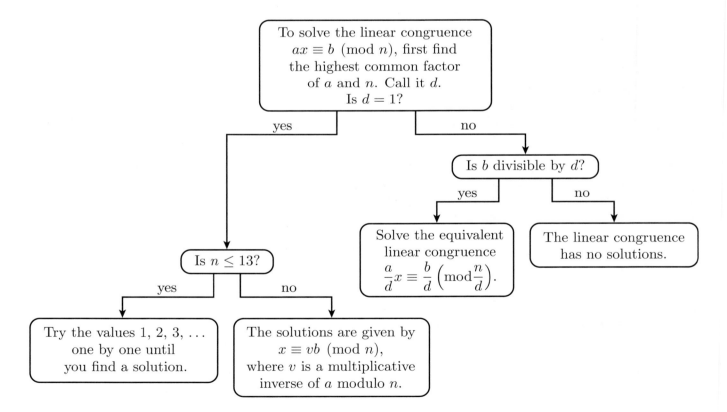

**Figure 13**   A decision tree for solving a linear congruence

**Activity 36**   *Solving a variety of linear congruences*

Solve the following linear congruences.

(a)  $5x \equiv 21 \pmod 9$        (b)  $11x \equiv 6 \pmod{38}$

(c)  $21x \equiv 14 \pmod{30}$        (d)  $-48x \equiv 24 \pmod{28}$

## 3.4   Affine ciphers

Usually, when a sensitive message is transmitted, it is first transformed to disguise it from all but the intended recipients. The algorithm used to transform a message is called a **cipher**, and the design of ciphers is called **cryptography**. Ciphers have been used throughout history for military and diplomatic communications and, in recent years, they have been increasingly used to protect the electronic transfer of confidential information and money.

Here you'll learn about one particular type of cipher, called an *affine cipher*, which uses some of the theory of linear congruences developed earlier. Although it is too basic a cipher to be used for sensitive information, many of the features of affine ciphers are shared by more sophisticated ciphers.

Before you can apply an affine cipher, or a cipher of a similar type, you must first replace the letters of the message you wish to transmit by numbers. Throughout this subsection we use Table 1 to switch between letters and numbers.

**Table 1**   A conversion table for letters and numbers

| A | B | C | D | E | F | G | H | I | J | K | L | M |
|---|---|---|---|---|---|---|---|---|---|---|---|---|
| 0 | 1 | 2 | 3 | 4 | 5 | 6 | 7 | 8 | 9 | 10 | 11 | 12 |

| N | O | P | Q | R | S | T | U | V | W | X | Y | Z |
|---|---|---|---|---|---|---|---|---|---|---|---|---|
| 13 | 14 | 15 | 16 | 17 | 18 | 19 | 20 | 21 | 22 | 23 | 24 | 25 |

For example, using Table 1 you can write the message

HULLABALOO

as

$7, 20, 11, 11, 0, 1, 0, 11, 14, 14.$

Now suppose that we wish to apply a cipher to this message; this process is called **enciphering**. Many simple ciphers consist of a rule for reordering the integers $0, 1, 2, \ldots, 25$ to disguise the message. For instance, you may have a rule that says you should replace the integer $x$ with the integer $E(x)$ from $0, 1, 2, \ldots, 25$ that satisfies

$$E(x) \equiv 5x + 23 \pmod{26}.$$

Using this rule,

$$E(0) = 23, \qquad \text{as } 5 \times 0 + 23 \equiv 23 \pmod{26},$$
$$E(1) = 2, \qquad \text{as } 5 \times 1 + 23 \equiv 28 \equiv 2 \pmod{26},$$
$$E(2) = 7, \qquad \text{as } 5 \times 2 + 23 \equiv 33 \equiv 7 \pmod{26},$$

and so on. Our message $7, 20, 11, 11, 0, 1, 0, 11, 14, 14$ becomes

$$
\begin{array}{cccccccccc}
7, & 20, & 11, & 11, & 0, & 1, & 0, & 11, & 14, & 14 \\
\downarrow & \downarrow & \downarrow & \downarrow & \downarrow & \downarrow & \downarrow & \downarrow & \downarrow & \downarrow \\
6, & 19, & 0, & 0, & 23, & 2, & 23, & 0, & 15, & 15.
\end{array}
$$

You can check this yourself. To do so, it may help you to notice that $23 \equiv -3 \pmod{26}$, so the rule for enciphering the message can be rewritten as

$$E(x) \equiv 5x - 3 \pmod{26}.$$

This cipher is an example of an affine cipher.

> **Affine ciphers**
>
> An **affine cipher** modulo 26 is a rule $E$ for reordering the integers $0, 1, 2, \ldots, 25$ given by
>
> $$E(x) \equiv ax + b \pmod{26},$$
>
> where $a$ and $b$ are integers, and $a$ and 26 are coprime.

This definition only allows affine ciphers modulo 26, because the only ciphers you'll meet here are those that use the 26 letters of the alphabet represented by integers in Table 1. To encipher a message that uses a different set of characters you can use an affine cipher of the form $E(x) \equiv ax + b \pmod{n}$, where $n$ is the number of characters you wish to choose from, and $a$ and $n$ are coprime.

The integers $a$ and 26 must be coprime so that $a$ has a multiplicative inverse modulo 26. The significance of this will be made clear shortly. For now, you may like to practise enciphering a message using an affine cipher.

**Activity 37** *Enciphering a message with an affine cipher*

Using Table 1 and the affine cipher

$$E(x) \equiv 3x + 14 \pmod{26},$$

encipher the message BROUHAHA.

The process of recovering the original message from an enciphered message is called **deciphering**. With affine ciphers, it's possible to decipher a message if you know the particular affine cipher used to encipher the message. For example, suppose that you receive the message

$$6, 19, 0, 0, 23, 2, 23, 0, 15, 15,$$

which you know has been created using the affine cipher $E(x) \equiv 5x + 23 \pmod{26}$ considered earlier. To decipher the first integer from this message, namely 6, you must find the integer $x$ from $0, 1, 2, \ldots, 25$ that satisfies $E(x) = 6$. That is, you must solve the congruence

$$5x + 23 \equiv 6 \pmod{26}.$$

To find $x$, first subtract 23 from both sides of the congruence. Since $6 - 23 \equiv -17 \equiv 9 \pmod{26}$, you obtain

$$5x \equiv 9 \pmod{26}.$$

This is a linear congruence. It follows from the results in the previous subsection that this can be solved, since 5 and 26 are coprime, and the solutions are given by

$$x \equiv 9v \pmod{26},$$

where $v$ is a multiplicative inverse of 5 modulo 26. The simplest way to find a value for $v$ is to observe that

$$5 \times 5 \equiv 25 \equiv -1 \pmod{26},$$

so

$$(-5) \times 5 \equiv 1 \pmod{26}$$

and hence $-5$ is a multiplicative inverse of 5 modulo 26.
(Since $21 \equiv -5 \pmod{26}$, the integer 21 is also a multiplicative inverse of 5 modulo 26; however, it's easier to use $-5$.) So the solutions are given by

$$x \equiv (-5) \times 9 \equiv -45 \equiv 7 \pmod{26}$$

and hence $x$ is the integer 7.

You could decipher each of the integers of the enciphered message in this way to recover the original message. If you were to do so, then you would find that you perform a similar set of operations each time. A quicker method to decipher the whole message is to obtain a 'deciphering rule' $D$ that undoes the enciphering rule $E$. Let's explain how to find $D$. Suppose that you wish to decipher the integer $y$. (You've just seen how to decipher the integer 6.) You must find the integer $x$ that satisfies $E(x) = y$. That is, you must solve the congruence

$$5x + 23 \equiv y \ (\mathrm{mod} \ 26).$$

Subtracting 23 from both sides gives

$$5x \equiv y - 23 \ (\mathrm{mod} \ 26).$$

Multiplying both sides by $-5$, which as you've seen is a multiplicative inverse of 5 modulo 26, gives

$$x \equiv -5(y - 23) \ (\mathrm{mod} \ 26).$$

So the rule $D$ that undoes the transformation $E$ is given by

$$D(y) \equiv -5(y - 23) \ (\mathrm{mod} \ 26).$$

This strategy for obtaining a deciphering rule works for *any* affine cipher.

### Deciphering rule for affine ciphers

The rule $D$ for deciphering the affine cipher $E(x) \equiv ax + b \ (\mathrm{mod} \ 26)$ is given by

$$D(y) \equiv v(y - b) \ (\mathrm{mod} \ 26),$$

where $v$ is any multiplicative inverse of $a$ modulo 26.

In the terminology of sets and functions, $E$ is a one-to-one function and $D$ is the inverse function of $E$.

**Example 16**   *Deciphering a message that has been enciphered using an affine cipher*

Suppose you receive the enciphered message $3, 17, 18, 7$, which you know has been created using the affine cipher

$$E(x) \equiv 9x + 21 \pmod{26}.$$

What does the message say?

**Solution**

🔍 Write down a rule for deciphering the message. 💭

A rule $D$ for deciphering the message is given by

$$D(y) \equiv v(y - 21) \pmod{26},$$

where $v$ is a multiplicative inverse of 9 modulo 26.

🔍 Find a multiplicative inverse of 9 modulo 26. You could apply Euclid's algorithm and backwards substitution, but it's quicker to notice that $3 \times 9 = 27$. 💭

Since

$$3 \times 9 \equiv 27 \equiv 1 \pmod{26},$$

we see that 3 is a multiplicative inverse of 9 modulo 26. So

$$D(y) \equiv 3(y - 21) \equiv 3(y + 5) \pmod{26}.$$

🔍 Use the deciphering rule to decipher the message. 💭

Hence

$$D(3) \equiv 3(3 + 5) \equiv 24 \pmod{26},$$
$$D(17) \equiv 3(17 + 5) \equiv 66 \equiv 14 \pmod{26},$$
$$D(18) \equiv 3(18 + 5) \equiv 69 \equiv 17 \pmod{26},$$
$$D(7) \equiv 3(7 + 5) \equiv 36 \equiv 10 \pmod{26}.$$

So the deciphered message is

$$24, 14, 17, 10,$$

which, by Table 1, says

YORK.

**Activity 38**   *Deciphering messages that have been enciphered using affine ciphers*

Suppose you receive the following two messages that have been enciphered using the specified affine cipher $E$. What do the messages say?

(a)  $14, 10, 6, 22, 22$, using $E(x) \equiv 5x + 10 \pmod{26}$

(b)  $22, 8, 11, 22, 9$, using $E(x) \equiv -9x + 6 \pmod{26}$

The ciphers that you have met in this section have all been very simple and you could have cracked them without using modular arithmetic. The ideas that you have met, however, are used in the construction of more sophisticated ciphers.

## The RSA factorising challenge

RSA ciphers are widely used in computing, business and military communication. They are named after Ron Rivest, Adi Shamir and Leonard Adleman who developed the algorithm in 1977. Modular arithmetic is a fundamental tool in RSA ciphers, as it is in many ciphers.

To encipher a message using the RSA algorithm, you must first choose two large prime numbers $p$ and $q$, and form their product $n = pq$. The integer $n$ can be made public, but $p$ and $q$ must remain secret. If $p$ and $q$ are discovered, then the cipher can be cracked. If $p$ and $q$ are sufficiently large, then it is extremely difficult to find them even if you know the value of $n$. In 1991, RSA Laboratories published a list of around fifty integers $n$, each a product of two primes, with a challenge to factorise them. Cash prizes were offered for factorising some of the larger numbers.

The smallest number in the list is known as RSA-100 because it has 100 digits. It is

$$1522605027922533360535618378132637429718068114961380688657908494580122963258952897654000350692006139.$$

Within a month of the challenge opening, RSA-100 had been factorised into two primes:

$$37975227936943673922808872755445627854565536638199$$
$$\times\ 40094690950920881030683735292761468389214899724061.$$

By 2007, when the challenge finished, fewer than half the numbers in the list had been factorised.

# Learning outcomes

After studying this unit, you should be able to:

- find quotients and remainders from integer division
- apply Euclid's algorithm and backwards substitution
- understand the definitions of congruences, residue classes and least residues
- add and subtract integers modulo $n$
- multiply integers and calculate powers modulo $n$
- understand and apply Fermat's little theorem
- test whether an integer is divisible by 3 or 9
- check whether 10-digit ISBNs are valid
- determine multiplicative inverses modulo $n$
- solve linear congruences
- encipher and decipher messages using affine ciphers.

# Solutions to activities

## Solution to Activity 1

(a) The quotient $q = 8$ and the remainder $r = 3$. So the equation $a = qn + r$ is
$$59 = 8 \times 7 + 3.$$

(b) $q = 7$, $r = 0$, and so $84 = 7 \times 12 + 0$.

(c) $q = 11$, $r = 1$, and so $100 = 11 \times 9 + 1$.

(d) $q = 0$, $r = 9$, and so $9 = 0 \times 100 + 9$.

(e) $q = 0$, $r = 0$, and so $0 = 0 \times 11 + 0$.

(f) $q = -12$, $r = 2$, and so $-58 = -12 \times 5 + 2$.

(g) $q = -12$, $r = 8$, and so $-100 = -12 \times 9 + 8$.

(h) $q = -8$, $r = 0$, and so $-96 = -8 \times 12 + 0$.

(i) $q = -1$, $r = 1$, and so $-4 = -1 \times 5 + 1$.

## Solution to Activity 2

(a) Euclid's algorithm gives
$$93 = 4 \times 21 + 9$$
$$21 = 2 \times 9 + 3$$
$$9 = 3 \times 3 + 0.$$
So the highest common factor of 93 and 21 is 3.

(b) Euclid's algorithm gives
$$138 = 2 \times 61 + 16$$
$$61 = 3 \times 16 + 13$$
$$16 = 1 \times 13 + 3$$
$$13 = 4 \times 3 + 1$$
$$3 = 3 \times 1 + 0.$$
So the highest common factor of 138 and 61 is 1.

(c) Euclid's algorithm gives
$$231 = 4 \times 49 + 35$$
$$49 = 1 \times 35 + 14$$
$$35 = 2 \times 14 + 7$$
$$14 = 2 \times 7 + 0.$$
So the highest common factor of 231 and 49 is 7.

## Solution to Activity 3

(a) Euclid's algorithm gives
$$93 = 2 \times 42 + 9$$
$$42 = 4 \times 9 + 6$$
$$9 = 1 \times 6 + 3$$
$$6 = 2 \times 3 + 0.$$

So the highest common factor of 93 and 42 is 3. Rearranging the equations gives
$$\boxed{9} = \boxed{93} - 2 \times \boxed{42}$$
$$\boxed{6} = \boxed{42} - 4 \times \boxed{9}$$
$$\boxed{3} = \boxed{9} - 1 \times \boxed{6}.$$
Backwards substitution gives
$$\boxed{3} = \boxed{9} - \left(\boxed{42} - 4 \times \boxed{9}\right)$$
$$= 5 \times \boxed{9} - \boxed{42}$$
$$= 5 \times \left(\boxed{93} - 2 \times \boxed{42}\right) - \boxed{42}$$
$$= 5 \times \boxed{93} - 11 \times \boxed{42}.$$
So $93 \times 5 + 42 \times (-11) = 3$. This is the equation $93v + 42w = d$ with $v = 5$ and $w = -11$.

(Check: $93 \times 5 + 42 \times (-11) = 465 - 462 = 3$.)

(b) Euclid's algorithm gives
$$70 = 2 \times 29 + 12$$
$$29 = 2 \times 12 + 5$$
$$12 = 2 \times 5 + 2$$
$$5 = 2 \times 2 + 1$$
$$2 = 2 \times 1 + 0.$$

The highest common factor of 70 and 29 is 1. Rearranging the equations gives
$$\boxed{12} = \boxed{70} - 2 \times \boxed{29}$$
$$\boxed{5} = \boxed{29} - 2 \times \boxed{12}$$
$$\boxed{2} = \boxed{12} - 2 \times \boxed{5}$$
$$\boxed{1} = \boxed{5} - 2 \times \boxed{2}.$$
Backwards substitution gives
$$\boxed{1} = \boxed{5} - 2 \times \left(\boxed{12} - 2 \times \boxed{5}\right)$$
$$= 5 \times \boxed{5} - 2 \times \boxed{12}$$
$$= 5 \times \left(\boxed{29} - 2 \times \boxed{12}\right) - 2 \times \boxed{12}$$
$$= 5 \times \boxed{29} - 12 \times \boxed{12}$$
$$= 5 \times \boxed{29} - 12 \times \left(\boxed{70} - 2 \times \boxed{29}\right)$$
$$= 29 \times \boxed{29} - 12 \times \boxed{70}.$$

So $70 \times (-12) + 29 \times 29 = 1$. This is the equation $70v + 29w = d$ with $v = -12$ and $w = 29$.

(Check:
$70 \times (-12) + 29 \times 29 = -840 + 841 = 1$.)

## Solution to Activity 4

(a) Euclid's algorithm gives
$$112 = 1 \times 91 + 21$$
$$91 = 4 \times 21 + 7$$
$$21 = 3 \times 7 + 0.$$

So the HCF of 112 and 91 is 7, and hence the HCF of $-112$ and $-91$ is also 7.

Rearranging the equations gives
$$\boxed{21} = \boxed{112} - 1 \times \boxed{91}$$
$$\boxed{7} = \boxed{91} - 4 \times \boxed{21}.$$

Backwards substitution gives
$$\boxed{7} = \boxed{91} - 4 \times \left(\boxed{112} - 1 \times \boxed{91}\right)$$
$$= 5 \times \boxed{91} - 4 \times \boxed{112}.$$

So
$$-112 \times 4 - 91 \times (-5) = 7.$$

This is the equation $-112v - 91w = d$ with $v = 4$ and $w = -5$.

(Check:
$-112 \times 4 - 91 \times (-5) = -448 + 455 = 7$.)

(b) Euclid's algorithm gives
$$105 = 2 \times 39 + 27$$
$$39 = 1 \times 27 + 12$$
$$27 = 2 \times 12 + 3$$
$$12 = 4 \times 3 + 0.$$

So the HCF of 105 and 39 is 3, and hence the HCF of $-105$ and 39 is also 3. Rearranging the equations gives
$$\boxed{27} = \boxed{105} - 2 \times \boxed{39}$$
$$\boxed{12} = \boxed{39} - 1 \times \boxed{27}$$
$$\boxed{3} = \boxed{27} - 2 \times \boxed{12}.$$

Backwards substitution gives
$$\boxed{3} = \boxed{27} - 2 \times \left(\boxed{39} - 1 \times \boxed{27}\right)$$
$$= 3 \times \boxed{27} - 2 \times \boxed{39}$$
$$= 3 \times \left(\boxed{105} - 2 \times \boxed{39}\right) - 2 \times \boxed{39}$$
$$= 3 \times \boxed{105} - 8 \times \boxed{39}.$$

So
$$-105 \times (-3) + 39 \times (-8) = 3.$$

This is the equation $-105v + 39w = d$ with $v = -3$ and $w = -8$.

(Check:
$-105 \times (-3) + 39 \times (-8) = 315 - 312 = 3$.)

## Solution to Activity 5

In order to obtain 1 litre of water in the cauldron in this way, we would need to find integers $v$ and $w$ such that
$$23v + 16w = 1.$$

It is easy to see that the highest common factor of the integers 23 and 16 is 1 and so the existence of such integers $v$ and $w$ follows from Bézout's identity. So it is possible to obtain 1 litre of water in the cauldron in this way.

In order to describe how to do this, we find the integers $v$ and $w$ in the usual way. Euclid's algorithm gives
$$23 = 1 \times 16 + 7$$
$$16 = 2 \times 7 + 2$$
$$7 = 3 \times 2 + 1$$
$$2 = 2 \times 1 + 0.$$

Rearranging the equations gives
$$\boxed{7} = \boxed{23} - 1 \times \boxed{16}$$
$$\boxed{2} = \boxed{16} - 2 \times \boxed{7}$$
$$\boxed{1} = \boxed{7} - 3 \times \boxed{2}.$$

Backwards substitution gives
$$\boxed{1} = \boxed{7} - 3 \times \left(\boxed{16} - 2 \times \boxed{7}\right)$$
$$= 7 \times \boxed{7} - 3 \times \boxed{16}$$
$$= 7 \times \left(\boxed{23} - 1 \times \boxed{16}\right) - 3 \times \boxed{16}$$
$$= 7 \times \boxed{23} - 10 \times \boxed{16}.$$

So

$$23 \times 7 + 16 \times (-10) = 1.$$

So if we fill the 23-litre bucket from the tap and pour it into the cauldron 7 times, then fill the 16-litre bucket from the cauldron and empty it out 10 times, we will be left with 1 litre of water in the cauldron.

## Solution to Activity 7

(a) True: 11 and 26 each have remainder 1 on division by 5.

(b) False: 9 has remainder 4 on division by 5 and $-9$ has remainder 1 on division by 5.

(c) True: 28 and 0 each have remainder 0 on division by 7.

(d) True: $-4$ and $-18$ each have remainder 3 on division by 7.

(e) True: $-8$ and 5 each have remainder 5 on division by 13.

(f) False: 38 is not divisible by 13.

## Solution to Activity 8

(a) The final digit of a positive integer is the remainder that we obtain when we divide that integer by 10. It follows that to check whether two positive integers are congruent modulo 10, we just need to check whether their final digits are equal.

(b) The method described in (a) doesn't work when we compare a positive integer with a negative integer. For example, $-17$ and 27 both have final digit 7, but they are not congruent modulo 10, because $-17$ has remainder 3 (not 7) when divided by 10.

## Solution to Activity 9

(a) True: $63 - 14 = 49$, which is divisible by 7.

(b) False: $-39 - 39 = -78$, which is not divisible by 7.

(c) False: $63 - 14 = 49$, which is not divisible by 12.

(d) True: $-8 - 16 = -24$, which is divisible by 12.

(e) True: $-30 - (-17) = -13$, which is divisible by 13.

(f) True: $43 - (-87) = 130$, which is divisible by 13.

## Solution to Activity 10

If $a$ is an odd number, then we can write $a = 1 + 2k$ for some integer $k$. This means that $a \equiv 1 \pmod{2}$.

If $a$ is an even number, then we can write $a = 2k$, or $a = 0 + 2k$, for some integer $k$. This means that $a \equiv 0 \pmod{2}$.

## Solution to Activity 11

(a) False: $-7$ and 7 are not congruent modulo 10, because $7 - (-7) = 14$, and 14 is not divisible by 10.

(b) True: $-17$, 3, 31 and 67 are all odd integers, so each has a remainder 1 when divided by 2.

(c) True: $-84$, 0 and 108 each have a remainder 0 when divided by 12.

## Solution to Activity 12

(a)

(b)

(c)

(d)

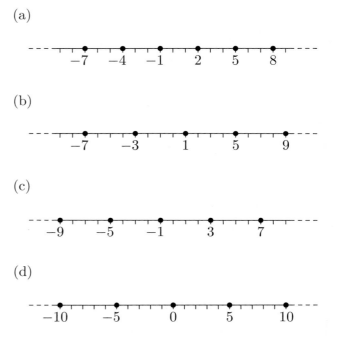

## Solution to Activity 13

(a) Since $17 = 1 \times 10 + 7$, the least residue is 7.

(b) Since $50 = 5 \times 10 + 0$, the least residue is 0.

(c) Since $6 = 0 \times 10 + 6$, the least residue is 6.

(d) Since $-1 = (-1) \times 10 + 9$, the least residue is 9.

(e) Since $-38 = (-4) \times 10 + 2$, the least residue is 2.

## Solution to Activity 14

(a) Since $17 = 5 \times 3 + 2$, the least residue is 2.

(b) Since $9 = 3 \times 3 + 0$, the least residue is 0.

(c) Since $-2 = (-1) \times 3 + 1$, the least residue is 1.

(d) Since $-10 = (-4) \times 3 + 2$, the least residue is 2.

(e) Since $3 = 1 \times 3 + 0$, the least residue is 0.

## Solution to Activity 15

There are 7 days in a week and so, in 1000 days' time, the day will be the same as it is today plus the remainder that you obtain when you divide 1000 by 7 (that is, the least residue of 1000 modulo 7). When you divide 1000 by 7 you obtain a remainder of 6. Therefore $1000 \equiv 6 \pmod 7$. Since $6 \equiv -1 \pmod 7$, it follows that in 1000 days' time it will be the same day as yesterday!

## Solution to Activity 16

(a) $7 + 3 \equiv 10 \equiv 4 \pmod 6$

So the least residue is 4.

(The statement 'So the least residue is ...' is omitted in solutions to subsequent parts of this activity. We follow a similar convention in later activities.)

(b) $7 - 3 \equiv 4 \pmod 6$

(c) $23 - 24 \equiv -1 \equiv 5 \pmod 6$

(d) $-3 - 19 \equiv 3 - 1 \equiv 2 \pmod 6$

(e) $67 + 68 \equiv 1 + 2 \equiv 3 \pmod 6$

(f) $601 - 6001 \equiv 1 - 1 \equiv 0 \pmod 6$

## Solution to Activity 17

(a) $6 + 4 \equiv 10 \equiv 0 \pmod{10}$

(b) $14 - 7 \equiv 7 \pmod{10}$

(c) $13 - 15 \equiv -2 \equiv 8 \pmod{10}$

(d) $-21 - 17 \equiv -1 - 7 \equiv -8 \equiv 2 \pmod{10}$

(e) $101 + 11 + 1 \equiv 1 + 1 + 1 \equiv 3 \pmod{10}$

(f) $101 - 11 - 1 \equiv 1 - 1 - 1 \equiv -1 \equiv 9 \pmod{10}$

## Solution to Activity 18

(a) $3 \times 6 \equiv 18 \equiv 4 \pmod 7$

So the least residue is 4.

Here is an alternative solution.

$$3 \times 6 \equiv 3 \times (-1) \equiv -3 \equiv 4 \pmod 7$$

Again, we see that the least residue is 4.

There are many other solutions to this problem, as there are to the other parts of this activity. Your solutions may differ from those that are given.

(b) $22 \times 29 \equiv 1 \times 1 \equiv 1 \pmod 7$

(c) $(-5) \times 16 \equiv 2 \times 2 \equiv 4 \pmod 7$

(d) $51 \times 74 \equiv 2 \times 4 \equiv 8 \equiv 1 \pmod 7$

(e) $47 \times (-25) \equiv (-2) \times 3 \equiv -6 \equiv 1 \pmod 7$

(f) $(-29) \times (-44) \equiv 29 \times 44 \equiv 1 \times 2 \equiv 2 \pmod 7$

## Solution to Activity 19

(a) $4 \times 4 \equiv 16 \equiv 0 \pmod 8$

(b) $17 \times 26 \equiv 1 \times 2 \equiv 2 \pmod 8$

(c) $(-6) \times 34 \equiv 2 \times 2 \equiv 4 \pmod 8$

(d) $16 \times 457 \equiv 0 \times 457 \equiv 0 \pmod 8$

(e) $47 \times (-25) \equiv (-1) \times (-1) \equiv 1 \pmod 8$

(f) $(-61) \times (-46) \equiv 61 \times 46$
$$\equiv (-3) \times (-2)$$
$$\equiv 6 \pmod 8$$

**Solution to Activity 20**

(a) Since $25 \equiv 1 \pmod 6$, it follows that
$$25^{25} \equiv 1^{25} \equiv 1 \pmod 6.$$
So the least residue is 1.

(b) Since $-9 \equiv 3 \pmod 6$, it follows that
$$(-9)^4 \equiv 3^4 \pmod 6.$$
Calculating powers of 3 gives
$$3^2 = 9$$
and so
$$3^2 \equiv 3 \pmod 6.$$
Therefore
$$3^4 \equiv 3^2 \times 3^2 \equiv 3 \times 3 \equiv 9 \equiv 3 \pmod 6.$$
In summary,
$$(-9)^4 \equiv 3 \pmod 6.$$
So the least residue is 3.

(c) Since $20 \equiv 2 \pmod 6$, it follows that
$$20^6 \equiv 2^6 \pmod 6.$$
Calculating powers of 2 gives
$$2^2 = 4 \text{ and } 2^3 = 8$$
and so
$$2^3 \equiv 2 \pmod 6.$$
Therefore
$$2^6 \equiv 2^3 \times 2^3 \equiv 2 \times 2 \equiv 4 \pmod 6.$$
In summary,
$$20^6 \equiv 4 \pmod 6.$$
So the least residue is 4.

**Solution to Activity 21**

(a) Since $25 \equiv -1 \pmod{13}$, it follows that
$$25^{25} \equiv (-1)^{25} \equiv -1 \equiv 12 \pmod{13}.$$
So the least residue is 12.

(b) Since $54 \equiv 2 \pmod{13}$, it follows that
$$54^4 \equiv 2^4 \equiv 16 \equiv 3 \pmod{13}.$$
So the least residue is 3.

(c) Since $16 \equiv 3 \pmod{13}$, it follows that
$$16^9 \equiv 3^9 \pmod{13}.$$
Calculating powers of 3 gives
$$3^2 = 9 \text{ and } 3^3 = 27$$
and so
$$3^3 \equiv 1 \pmod{13}.$$
Therefore
$$3^9 \equiv 3^3 \times 3^3 \times 3^3 \equiv 1^3 \equiv 1 \pmod{13}.$$
In summary,
$$16^9 \equiv 1 \pmod{13}.$$
So the least residue is 1.

**Solution to Activity 22**

(a) Since $1^4 = 1$, the least residue is 1.

(b) Since
$$2^4 \equiv 16 \equiv 1 \pmod 5,$$
the least residue is 1.

(c) Since
$$3^4 \equiv (-2)^4 \equiv 16 \equiv 1 \pmod 5,$$
the least residue is 1.

(Alternatively, since
$$3^4 \equiv 81 \equiv 1 \pmod 5,$$
the least residue is 1.)

(d) Since
$$4^4 \equiv (-1)^4 \equiv 1 \pmod 5,$$
the least residue is 1.

(e) Since $7 \equiv 2 \pmod 5$ it follows from part (b) that
$$7^4 \equiv 2^4 \equiv 1 \pmod 5.$$
So the least residue is 1.

## Solution to Activity 23

(a) By Fermat's little theorem,
$$5^6 \equiv 1 \pmod{7}.$$
So the least residue is 1.

(b) First, $18 \equiv 4 \pmod{7}$ so
$$18^{18} \equiv 4^{18} \pmod{7}.$$
By Fermat's little theorem,
$$4^6 \equiv 1 \pmod{7}.$$
Since $18 = 3 \times 6$, we obtain
$$4^{18} \equiv (4^6)^3$$
$$\equiv 1^3$$
$$\equiv 1 \pmod{7}.$$
So the least residue is 1.

(c) First, $-11 \equiv 3 \pmod{7}$ so
$$(-11)^{33} \equiv 3^{33} \pmod{7}.$$
By Fermat's little theorem,
$$3^6 \equiv 1 \pmod{7}.$$
Since $33 = 5 \times 6 + 3$, we obtain
$$3^{33} \equiv (3^6)^5 \times 3^3$$
$$\equiv 1^5 \times 3^3$$
$$\equiv 27$$
$$\equiv 6 \pmod{7}.$$
So the least residue is 6.

## Solution to Activity 24

(a) By Fermat's little theorem,
$$7^{10} \equiv 1 \pmod{11}.$$
So the least residue is 1.

(b) First, $-5 \equiv 6 \pmod{11}$ so
$$(-5)^{31} \equiv 6^{31} \pmod{11}.$$
By Fermat's little theorem,
$$6^{10} \equiv 1 \pmod{11}.$$
Since $31 = 3 \times 10 + 1$, we obtain
$$6^{31} \equiv (6^{10})^3 \times 6^1$$
$$\equiv 1^3 \times 6$$
$$\equiv 6 \pmod{11}.$$
So the least residue is 6.

(c) First, $13 \equiv 2 \pmod{11}$ so
$$13^{85} \equiv 2^{85} \pmod{11}.$$
By Fermat's little theorem,
$$2^{10} \equiv 1 \pmod{11}.$$
Since $85 = 8 \times 10 + 5$, we obtain
$$2^{85} \equiv (2^{10})^8 \times 2^5$$
$$\equiv 1^8 \times 2^5$$
$$\equiv 32$$
$$\equiv 10 \pmod{11}.$$
So the least residue is 10.

## Solution to Activity 25

(a) The digit sum of 982 is $9 + 8 + 2 = 19$. This is not divisible by 3, so 982 is not divisible by 3.

(b) The digit sum of 753 is $7 + 5 + 3 = 15$. This is divisible by 3, so 753 is divisible by 3.

(c) The digit sum of 8364 is
$$8 + 3 + 6 + 4 = 21.$$
This is divisible by 3, so 8364 is divisible by 3.

(d) The digit sum of $-9245$ is
$$9 + 2 + 4 + 5 = 20.$$
This is not divisible by 3, so $-9245$ is not divisible by 3.

(e) The digit sum of 98 285 385 335 is
$$9 + 8 + 2 + 8 + 5 + 3 + 8 + 5 + 3 + 3 + 5 = 59.$$
The digit sum of 59 is $5 + 9 = 14$. This is not divisible by 3, so 59 is not divisible by 3, and hence 98 285 385 335 is not divisible by 3.

(f) The digits of $10^{100}$ consist of a single 1 and one hundred 0s. Therefore $10^{100}$ has digit sum 1, which is not divisible by 3, so $10^{100}$ is not divisible by 3.

**Solution to Activity 26**

(a)  The digit sum of 8469 is $8 + 4 + 6 + 9 = 27$. This is divisible by 9, so 8469 is divisible by 9.

(b)  The digit sum of 6172 is $6 + 1 + 7 + 2 = 16$. This is not divisible by 9, so 6172 is not divisible by 9.

(c)  The digit sum of 7 989 989 897 979 897 is
$$7 + 9 + 8 + 9 + 9 + 8 + 9 + 8$$
$$+ 9 + 7 + 9 + 7 + 9 + 8 + 9 + 7 = 132.$$

The digit sum of 132 is $1 + 3 + 2 = 6$. This is not divisible by 9, therefore 132 is not divisible by 9, and nor is 7 989 989 897 979 897.

**Solution to Activity 27**

(a)  $0 + 2 \cdot 0 + 3 \cdot 1 + 4 \cdot 6 + 5 \cdot 0$
$$+ 6 \cdot 6 + 7 \cdot 2 + 8 \cdot 1 + 9 \cdot 4 + 10 \cdot 0$$
$$\equiv 0 + 0 + 3 + 24 + 0 + 36 + 14 + 8 + 36 + 0$$
$$\equiv 0 + 0 + 3 + 2 + 0 + 3 + 3 + 8 + 3 + 0$$
$$\equiv 22$$
$$\equiv 0 \pmod{11}$$

So 0412606100 satisfies the ISBN congruence check.

(b)  $10 + 2 \cdot 8 + 3 \cdot 7 + 4 \cdot 2 + 5 \cdot 2$
$$+ 6 \cdot 4 + 7 \cdot 1 + 8 \cdot 0 + 9 \cdot 2 + 10 \cdot 0$$
$$\equiv 10 + 16 + 21 + 8 + 10 + 24 + 7 + 0 + 18 + 0$$
$$\equiv 10 + 5 + 10 + 8 + 10 + 2 + 7 + 0 + 7 + 0$$
$$\equiv 59$$
$$\not\equiv 0 \pmod{11}$$

So 020142278X does not satisfy the ISBN congruence check.

(c)  $9 + 2 \cdot 0 + 3 \cdot 8 + 4 \cdot 8 + 5 \cdot 1$
$$+ 6 \cdot 1 + 7 \cdot 1 + 8 \cdot 9 + 9 \cdot 6 + 10 \cdot 0$$
$$\equiv 9 + 0 + 24 + 32 + 5 + 6 + 7 + 72 + 54 + 0$$
$$\equiv 9 + 0 + 2 + 10 + 5 + 6 + 7 + 6 + 10 + 0$$
$$\equiv 55$$
$$\equiv 0 \pmod{11}$$

So 0691118809 satisfies the ISBN congruence check.

(Alternatively, the solutions to parts (a), (b) and (c) can be shortened by using congruences such as
$$10 \equiv -1 \pmod{11},$$
$$9 \equiv -2 \pmod{11},$$
$$8 \equiv -3 \pmod{11}.$$
For example, the congruences in (a) can be written as
$$0 + 2 \cdot 0 + 3 \cdot 1 + 4 \cdot 6 + 5 \cdot 0$$
$$- 5 \cdot 6 - 4 \cdot 2 - 3 \cdot 1 - 2 \cdot 4 - 1 \cdot 0$$
$$\equiv 0 + 0 + 3 + 24 + 0 - 30 - 8 - 3 - 8 + 0$$
$$\equiv -22$$
$$\equiv 0 \pmod{11}.)$$

**Solution to Activity 28**

(a)  Since
$$1 \times 1 \equiv 1 \pmod{9},$$
1 is itself a multiplicative inverse of 1 modulo 9.

(b)  Since
$$5 \times 2 \equiv 1 \pmod{9},$$
2 is a multiplicative inverse of 5 modulo 9.

(c)  Trying the values $1, 2, 3, \ldots$ one by one, we find that
$$7 \times 4 \equiv 28 \equiv 1 \pmod{9},$$
so 4 is a multiplicative inverse of 7 modulo 9.

(d)  Since
$$16 \equiv 7 \pmod{9},$$
16 has the same multiplicative inverse modulo 9 as 7, namely 4 (as you saw in part (c)), because
$$16 \times 4 \equiv 7 \times 4 \equiv 1 \pmod{9}.$$

## Solution to Activity 29

(a) The integer 0 doesn't have a multiplicative inverse modulo 9 because
$$0 \times v \equiv 0 \pmod 9$$
for any integer $v$.

(b) The congruence
$$6v \equiv 1 \pmod 9$$
is equivalent to the statement that
$$6v = 1 + 9k,$$
for some integer $k$. In this equation, the left-hand side is divisible by 3, but the right-hand side is not. This is impossible, so 6 does not have a multiplicative inverse modulo 9.

(Alternatively, suppose that $v$ is a multiplicative inverse of 6 modulo 9. Then $2v$ is a multiplicative inverse of 3 modulo 9 because
$$3 \times 2v \equiv 6v \equiv 1 \pmod 9.$$
However, we've seen already that 3 does *not* have a multiplicative inverse modulo 9, so in fact there is no such integer $v$. That is, 6 doesn't have a multiplicative inverse modulo 9 after all.)

(c) The integer 18 doesn't have a multiplicative inverse modulo 9 because $18 \equiv 0 \pmod 9$, so
$$18v \equiv 0 \times v \equiv 0 \pmod 9$$
for any integer $v$.

## Solution to Activity 30

(a) The integers 10 and 13 are coprime, so there is a multiplicative inverse of 10 modulo 13. Trying the values $2, 3, 4, \ldots$ one by one, we find that
$$4 \times 10 \equiv 40 \equiv 1 \pmod{13},$$
so 4 is a multiplicative inverse of 10 modulo 13.

(b) The integers 12 and 21 are not coprime (since both are divisible by 3), so there is no multiplicative inverse of 12 modulo 21.

(c) The integers 18 and 19 are coprime, so there is a multiplicative inverse of 18 modulo 19. Since $18 \equiv -1 \pmod{19}$ it follows that
$$18 \times 18 \equiv (-1) \times (-1) \equiv 1 \pmod{19}.$$
Therefore 18 is a multiplicative inverse of 18 modulo 19.

(d) The integers 0 and 11 are not coprime (since both are divisible by 11), so there is no multiplicative inverse of 0 modulo 11.

(Alternatively, since $0 \times v \equiv 0 \pmod{11}$, for any integer $v$, there is no multiplicative inverse of 0 modulo 11. Reasoning in the same way you see that 0 doesn't have a multiplicative inverse modulo $n$, for any integer $n$.)

(e) The integers 7 and 16 are coprime, so there is a multiplicative inverse of 7 modulo 16. Trying the values $2, 3, 4, \ldots$ one by one, we find that
$$7 \times 7 \equiv 49 \equiv 1 \pmod{16},$$
so 7 is a multiplicative inverse of 7 modulo 16.

(f) Euclid's algorithm gives
$$57 = 5 \times 10 + 7$$
$$10 = 1 \times 7 + 3$$
$$7 = 2 \times 3 + 1$$
$$3 = 3 \times 1 + 0.$$
A remainder 1 is obtained, so 10 and 57 are coprime, and hence 10 has a multiplicative inverse modulo 57. Rearranging the equations gives
$$\boxed{7} = \boxed{57} - 5 \times \boxed{10}$$
$$\boxed{3} = \boxed{10} - 1 \times \boxed{7}$$
$$\boxed{1} = \boxed{7} - 2 \times \boxed{3}.$$
Backwards substitution gives
$$\boxed{1} = \boxed{7} - 2 \times \left( \boxed{10} - 1 \times \boxed{7} \right)$$
$$= 3 \times \boxed{7} - 2 \times \boxed{10}$$
$$= 3 \times \left( \boxed{57} - 5 \times \boxed{10} \right) - 2 \times \boxed{10}$$
$$= 3 \times \boxed{57} - 17 \times \boxed{10}.$$
(Check: $3 \times 57 - 17 \times 10 = 171 - 170 = 1$.)

Hence
$$(-17) \times 10 \equiv 1 \pmod{57}$$
and so $-17$ is a multiplicative inverse of 10 modulo 57. Since
$$-17 \equiv 40 \pmod{57},$$
40 is also a multiplicative inverse of 10 modulo 57.

(g) Euclid's algorithm gives

$$217 = 2 \times 84 + 49$$
$$84 = 1 \times 49 + 35$$
$$49 = 1 \times 35 + 14$$
$$35 = 2 \times 14 + 7$$
$$14 = 2 \times 7 + 0.$$

So 7 is a factor of both 84 and 217, and hence there is no multiplicative inverse of 84 modulo 217.

(h) Euclid's algorithm gives

$$96 = 2 \times 43 + 10$$
$$43 = 4 \times 10 + 3$$
$$10 = 3 \times 3 + 1$$
$$3 = 3 \times 1 + 0.$$

A remainder 1 is obtained, so 43 and 96 are coprime, and hence 43 has a multiplicative inverse modulo 96. Rearranging the equations gives

$$\boxed{10} = \boxed{96} - 2 \times \boxed{43}$$
$$\boxed{3} = \boxed{43} - 4 \times \boxed{10}$$
$$\boxed{1} = \boxed{10} - 3 \times \boxed{3}.$$

Backwards substitution gives

$$\boxed{1} = \boxed{10} - 3 \times \left( \boxed{43} - 4 \times \boxed{10} \right)$$
$$= 13 \times \boxed{10} - 3 \times \boxed{43}$$
$$= 13 \times \left( \boxed{96} - 2 \times \boxed{43} \right) - 3 \times \boxed{43}$$
$$= 13 \times \boxed{96} - 29 \times \boxed{43}.$$

(Check: $13 \times 96 - 29 \times 43 = 1248 - 1247 = 1$.)

Hence

$$(-29) \times 43 \equiv 1 \ (\text{mod } 96),$$

and so $-29$ is a multiplicative inverse of 43 modulo 96. Since

$$-29 \equiv 67 \ (\text{mod } 96),$$

67 is also a multiplicative inverse of 43 modulo 96.

## Solution to Activity 31

(a) As 2 and 7 are coprime, the linear congruence has solutions. Trying the values $1, 2, 3, \ldots$ one by one, we find that

$$2 \times 6 \equiv 12 \equiv 5 \ (\text{mod } 7),$$

and so the solutions are given by

$$x \equiv 6 \ (\text{mod } 7).$$

(There is a clever alternative way of solving this linear congruence. Notice that

$$5 \equiv -2 \ (\text{mod } 7),$$

and so the linear congruence is equivalent to

$$2x \equiv -2 \ (\text{mod } 7).$$

Thus the solutions are given by

$$x \equiv -1 \equiv 6 \ (\text{mod } 7).)$$

(b) As 7 and 10 are coprime, the linear congruence has solutions. Trying the values $1, 2, 3, \ldots$ one by one, we find that

$$7 \times 4 \equiv 28 \equiv 8 \ (\text{mod } 10),$$

and so the solutions are given by

$$x \equiv 4 \ (\text{mod } 10).$$

(c) Since

$$15 \equiv 4 \ (\text{mod } 11) \quad \text{and} \quad -13 \equiv 9 \ (\text{mod } 11),$$

the linear congruence is equivalent to

$$4x \equiv 9 \ (\text{mod } 11).$$

As 4 and 9 are coprime, this linear congruence has solutions. Trying the values $1, 2, 3, \ldots$ one by one, we find that

$$4 \times 5 \equiv 20 \equiv 9 \ (\text{mod } 11),$$

and so the solutions are given by

$$x \equiv 5 \ (\text{mod } 11).$$

## Solution to Activity 32

(a) As 7 and 20 are coprime, the linear congruence has solutions. The solutions are given by
$$x \equiv 8v \pmod{20},$$
where $v$ is a multiplicative inverse of 7 modulo 20.

Since
$$3 \times 7 \equiv 21 \equiv 1 \pmod{20},$$
we see that 3 is a multiplicative inverse of 7 modulo 20. So the solutions are given by
$$x \equiv 8 \times 3 \equiv 24 \equiv 4 \pmod{20}.$$
(Check: $7 \times 4 \equiv 28 \equiv 8 \pmod{20}$.)

(If you don't guess the value 3 of a multiplicative inverse of 7 modulo 20, then you can calculate a multiplicative inverse using Euclid's algorithm and backwards substitution. This method is used to calculate multiplicative inverses in the remaining parts of this activity.)

(b) Since $-26 \equiv 8 \pmod{17}$, we can rewrite the linear congruence as
$$3x \equiv 8 \pmod{17}.$$
As 3 and 17 are coprime, the linear congruence has solutions. The solutions are given by
$$x \equiv 8v \pmod{17},$$
where $v$ is a multiplicative inverse of 3 modulo 17.

Euclid's algorithm gives
$$17 = 5 \times 3 + 2$$
$$3 = 1 \times 2 + 1.$$
Backwards substitution gives
$$1 = 3 - 2 = 3 - (17 - 5 \times 3) = 6 \times 3 - 17.$$
So
$$6 \times 3 \equiv 1 \pmod{17}$$
and hence 6 is a multiplicative inverse of 3 modulo 17. So the solutions are given by
$$x \equiv 8 \times 6 \equiv 48 \equiv 14 \pmod{17}.$$
(Check: $3 \times 14 \equiv 3 \times (-3) \equiv -9 \equiv 8 \pmod{17}$.)

(c) As 13 and 30 are coprime, the linear congruence has solutions. The solutions are given by
$$x \equiv 3v \pmod{30},$$
where $v$ is a multiplicative inverse of 13 modulo 30.

Euclid's algorithm gives
$$30 = 2 \times 13 + 4$$
$$13 = 3 \times 4 + 1.$$
Backwards substitution gives
$$1 = 13 - 3 \times 4$$
$$= 13 - 3 \times (30 - 2 \times 13)$$
$$= 7 \times 13 - 3 \times 30.$$
So
$$7 \times 13 \equiv 1 \pmod{30}$$
and hence 7 is a multiplicative inverse of 13 modulo 30. So the solutions are given by
$$x \equiv 3 \times 7 \equiv 21 \pmod{30}.$$
(Check:
$13 \times 21 \equiv 13 \times (-9) \equiv -117 \equiv 3 \pmod{30}$.)

## Solution to Activity 33

Let $N$ be the total number of coins. There are 6 coins left over when the $N$ coins are first shared out among the 10 pirates, so
$$N \equiv 6 \pmod{10}.$$
The second time the $N$ coins are shared out, among the remaining 7 pirates, there are no coins left over, so $N = 7x$, for some positive integer $x$. Substituting $N = 7x$ into the first congruence gives
$$7x \equiv 6 \pmod{10}.$$
Trying the values $1, 2, 3, \ldots$ one by one, we find that
$$7 \times 8 \equiv 56 \equiv 6 \pmod{10}$$
and so the possible solutions are given by
$$x \equiv 8 \pmod{10}.$$
Since the total number of coins $N = 7x$ is no more than 100, the only possibility is that $N = 7 \times 8 = 56$.

## Solution to Activity 34

(a) The highest common factor of 4 and 10 is 2. Since 5 is not divisible by 2, the linear congruence has no solutions.

(b) The highest common factor of $-12$ and 42 is 6. Since 8 is not divisible by 6, the linear congruence has no solutions.

(c) To find the highest common factor of 48 and 111, we apply Euclid's algorithm:
$$111 = 2 \times 48 + 15$$
$$48 = 3 \times 15 + 3$$
$$15 = 5 \times 3 + 0.$$

Therefore the highest common factor is 3. Since 70 is not divisible by 3, the linear congruence has no solutions.

## Solution to Activity 35

(a) The highest common factor of 12 and 15 is 3. Since 6 is also divisible by 3, the linear congruence can be solved and is equivalent to
$$4x \equiv 2 \ (\mathrm{mod}\ 5).$$
Trying the values $1, 2, 3, \ldots$ one by one, we find that
$$4 \times 3 \equiv 12 \equiv 2 \ (\mathrm{mod}\ 5).$$
So the solutions are given by
$$x \equiv 3 \ (\mathrm{mod}\ 5).$$
(Check: $4 \times 3 \equiv 12 \equiv 2 \ (\mathrm{mod}\ 5)$.)

(Alternatively, proceed as before to obtain the linear congruence
$$4x \equiv 2 \ (\mathrm{mod}\ 5).$$
Since $4 \equiv -1 \ (\mathrm{mod}\ 5)$, this linear congruence is equivalent to
$$-x \equiv 2 \ (\mathrm{mod}\ 5).$$
Hence the solutions are given by
$$x \equiv -2 \equiv 3 \ (\mathrm{mod}\ 5).)$$

(b) Since $-25 \equiv 15 \ (\mathrm{mod}\ 40)$, the linear congruence can be rewritten as
$$15x \equiv 10 \ (\mathrm{mod}\ 40).$$
The highest common factor of 15 and 40 is 5. Since 10 is also divisible by 5, this linear congruence has solutions and is equivalent to
$$3x \equiv 2 \ (\mathrm{mod}\ 8).$$
Trying the values $1, 2, 3, \ldots$ one by one, we find that
$$3 \times 6 \equiv 18 \equiv 2 \ (\mathrm{mod}\ 8).$$
So the solutions are given by
$$x \equiv 6 \ (\mathrm{mod}\ 8).$$
(Check: $3 \times 6 \equiv 18 \equiv 2 \ (\mathrm{mod}\ 8)$.)

(c) To find the highest common factor of 18 and 98, you could apply Euclid's algorithm, but it's probably easier to express each number as a product of prime factors: $18 = 2 \times 3^2$ and $98 = 2 \times 7^2$. You can see that the highest common factor is 2. Since 6 is divisible by 2, the linear congruence has solutions and is equivalent to
$$9x \equiv 3 \ (\mathrm{mod}\ 49).$$
The solutions of this linear congruence are given by
$$x \equiv 3v \ (\mathrm{mod}\ 49),$$
where $v$ is a multiplicative inverse of 9 modulo 49.

Euclid's algorithm gives
$$49 = 5 \times 9 + 4$$
$$9 = 2 \times 4 + 1.$$
Backwards substitution gives
$$1 = 9 - 2 \times 4$$
$$= 9 - 2(49 - 5 \times 9)$$
$$= 11 \times 9 - 2 \times 49.$$
So
$$11 \times 9 \equiv 1 \ (\mathrm{mod}\ 49),$$
and hence 11 is a multiplicative inverse of 9 modulo 49. So the solutions are given by
$$x \equiv 3 \times 11 \equiv 33 \ (\mathrm{mod}\ 49).$$
(Check:
$$9 \times 33 \equiv 9 \times (-16) \equiv -144 \equiv 3 \ (\mathrm{mod}\ 49).)$$

## Solution to Activity 36

(a) Since $21 \equiv 3 \pmod 9$, we can rewrite the linear congruence as
$$5x \equiv 3 \pmod 9.$$
As 5 and 9 are coprime, the linear congruence has solutions. Trying the values $1, 2, 3, \ldots$ one by one, we find that
$$5 \times 6 \equiv 30 \equiv 3 \pmod 9.$$
So the solutions are given by
$$x \equiv 6 \pmod 9.$$

(b) As 11 and 38 are coprime, the linear congruence has solutions. The solutions are given by
$$x \equiv 6v \pmod{38},$$
where $v$ is a multiplicative inverse of 11 modulo 38.

Euclid's algorithm gives
$$38 = 3 \times 11 + 5$$
$$11 = 2 \times 5 + 1.$$
Backwards substitution gives
$$1 = 11 - 2 \times 5$$
$$= 11 - 2(38 - 3 \times 11)$$
$$= 7 \times 11 - 2 \times 38.$$
So
$$7 \times 11 \equiv 1 \pmod{38}$$
and hence 7 is a multiplicative inverse of 11 modulo 38. So the solutions are given by
$$x \equiv 6 \times 7 \equiv 42 \equiv 4 \pmod{38}.$$
(Check: $11 \times 4 \equiv 44 \equiv 6 \pmod{38}$.)

(c) The highest common factor of 21 and 30 is 3. Since 14 is not divisible by 3, the linear congruence has no solutions.

(d) Since $-48 \equiv 8 \pmod{28}$, the linear congruence can be rewritten as
$$8x \equiv 24 \pmod{28}.$$
The highest common factor of 8 and 28 is 4. Since 24 is also divisible by 4, this linear congruence has solutions and is equivalent to
$$2x \equiv 6 \pmod 7.$$
Trying the values $1, 2, 3, \ldots$ one by one, we find that
$$2 \times 3 \equiv 6 \pmod 7.$$
So the solutions are given by
$$x \equiv 3 \pmod 7.$$
(Check: $2 \times 3 \equiv 6 \pmod 7$.)

## Solution to Activity 37

Using Table 1, the message BROUHAHA becomes
$$1, 17, 14, 20, 7, 0, 7, 0.$$
Next, applying the affine cipher
$$E(x) \equiv 3x + 14 \pmod{26},$$
we find that
$$E(1) \equiv 3 \times 1 + 14 \equiv 17 \pmod{26},$$
$$E(17) \equiv 3 \times 17 + 14 \equiv 65 \equiv 13 \pmod{26},$$
$$E(14) \equiv 3 \times 14 + 14 \equiv 56 \equiv 4 \pmod{26},$$
$$E(20) \equiv 3 \times 20 + 14 \equiv 74 \equiv 22 \pmod{26},$$
$$E(7) \equiv 3 \times 7 + 14 \equiv 35 \equiv 9 \pmod{26},$$
$$E(0) \equiv 3 \times 0 + 14 \equiv 14 \pmod{26}.$$
Therefore the enciphered message is
$$17, 13, 4, 22, 9, 14, 9, 14.$$

## Solution to Activity 38

(a) A rule $D$ for deciphering the message is given by
$$D(y) \equiv v(y - 10) \pmod{26},$$
where $v$ is a multiplicative inverse of 5 modulo 26.

Since
$$(-5) \times 5 \equiv -25 \equiv 1 \pmod{26},$$
we see that $-5$ is a multiplicative inverse of 5 modulo 26. (You can also use Euclid's algorithm and backwards substitution to find a multiplicative inverse of 5 modulo 26.) So
$$D(y) \equiv -5(y - 10) \pmod{26}.$$
Hence
$$D(14) \equiv -5(14 - 10) \equiv -20 \equiv 6 \pmod{26},$$
$$D(10) \equiv -5(10 - 10) \equiv 0 \pmod{26},$$
$$D(6) \equiv -5(6 - 10) \equiv 20 \pmod{26},$$
$$D(22) \equiv -5(22 - 10) \equiv -60 \equiv 18 \pmod{26}.$$
So the deciphered message is
$$6, 0, 20, 18, 18,$$
which, using Table 1, says
$$\text{GAUSS.}$$

(b)  A rule $D$ for deciphering the message is given by
$$D(y) \equiv v(y - 6) \ (\text{mod } 26),$$
where $v$ is a multiplicative inverse of $-9$ modulo 26.

Since
$$(-3) \times (-9) \equiv 27 \equiv 1 \ (\text{mod } 26),$$
we see that $-3$ is a multiplicative inverse of $-9$ modulo 26. (You can also use Euclid's algorithm and backwards substitution to find a multiplicative inverse of $-9$ modulo 26.) So
$$D(y) \equiv -3(y - 6) \ (\text{mod } 26).$$
Hence
$$D(22) \equiv -3(22 - 6) \equiv -48 \equiv 4 \ (\text{mod } 26),$$
$$D(8) \equiv -3(8 - 6) \equiv -6 \equiv 20 \ (\text{mod } 26),$$
$$D(11) \equiv -3(11 - 6) \equiv -15 \equiv 11 \ (\text{mod } 26),$$
$$D(9) \equiv -3(9 - 6) \equiv -9 \equiv 17 \ (\text{mod } 26).$$
So the deciphered message is
$$4, 20, 11, 4, 17,$$
which, using Table 1, says
EULER.

# Acknowledgements

Grateful acknowledgement is made to the following sources:

Page 154: Srinivasa Ramanujan: Konrad Jacobs / http://en.wikipedia.org/wiki/File:Srinivasa_Ramanujan_-_OPC_-_1.jpg. This file is licensed under the Creative Commons Attribution-Share Alike Licence http://creativecommons.org/licenses/by-sa/3.0

Every effort has been made to contact copyright holders. If any have been inadvertently overlooked the publishers will be pleased to make the necessary arrangements at the first opportunity.

# Index